D1485076

Claim Your Free Gift

www.questionsaboutme.com/free

Follow us on

@QuestionsAboutMe

@QuestionsAboutMe_Official

Questions & Customer Service

hello@questionsaboutme.com

3000 Unique Questions About Me by Questions About Me.com.

www.questionsaboutme.com

Introduction

Communication is key for meaningful relationships, but we often rely on small talk and dull conversations without really engaging one another.

3000 Unique Questions About Me is a tool to help spark engaging discussions and thoughts. No matter if it's with someone you've known for years or someone you recently met, use our *3000 Unique Questions About Me* book to unlock endless conversational possibilities.

The goal of this book is to enjoy learning more about yourself and foster conversation and engagement with others.

Ask these questions to yourself, use them as conversation prompts with family, friends, or even strangers to cultivate meaningful and fun discussions. Using the power of these questions, you can communicate and connect in a way that is easy and fun.

We have intentionally made the questions random so they're spontaneous. The questions have been created for adults, but they are suitable for children aged from nine years old with some easy questions intended for younger audiences.

Our Questions About Me series is for everyone- there's no adult content and the questions are also free from political affiliations and religious preferences.

How to Use this Book

» The format of this book is entirely flexible, and the questions can be tackled any way you like.

» You can skip around and answer whatever questions, or you can start at the beginning and work through all the questions in order.

» The writing space is purposely limited so you can use this book as a tool in various ways- ask the questions out aloud, fill it in, or leave it blank and answer the questions in your journal.

» Try to push beyond simple "yes" or "no" responses and go deeper with your answers, which will help lead you to rewarding explorations and discussions.

» Put down your phone, switch off the TV and declare the time you spend answering these questions a no judgment zone.

» Remember, there are no correct or incorrect answers. Allow yourself to be vulnerable and don't hold back on your responses.

There are numerous ways you can enjoy our Questions About Me series—on your own, one-on-one, or in a group setting.

Yourself

» Use as a simple guided journal, or question a day journal, for writing prompts or journaling starts for creative inspiration.
» Complete the questions as a mindfulness activity for self-reflection and personal growth and to help better understand yourself.
» Leave a completed book to someone special as a keepsake.
» Makes a unique and thoughtful gift idea for any occasion for your friends, your family, significant other or for yourself.

One-on-one

» Take turns asking questions with your significant other. Strengthen your relationship and bond with your partner as you learn more about each other. You can also get your partner to answer the questions as if they were you.
» Deepen your knowledge about those closest you. Discover new things about your kids, parents, siblings, and close friends with questions you never thought to ask.

Group discussions

» Stir up inspiring conversations at gatherings with family or friends at the dinner table, family events, or as a holiday activity.
» Download the eBook and use while traveling on road trips or as a vacation activity.
» Level up your conversation skills at networking events, team building games, business trips, ice breaker activities, job interviews, or therapy sessions.

The most important thing to know about using this book is: **There is no wrong way to use this book.** What's important is that you have fun with it.

No matter how you choose to use this book, enjoy using our Questions About Me series in any context or social situation to ignite meaningful connections and conversations.

www.questionsaboutme.com

01   "It's not what you know, it's who you know." Is that true?

02   What was the last thing that blew your mind?

03   If given the opportunity, would you have a psychic reading?

04   Your colleagues have just given you a round of applause. What have you done?

05   What's the last thing you Googled?

06   Other than when you're sick, have you ever spent an entire day in your pajamas? When was the last time?

07   If you were a gemstone, which one would you be, and why?

08   What's your favorite heroic animal story?

09   Justin Hayward sang "Forever Autumn" in 1976. What season would you like it to be forever?

10   What happened on your most manic Monday?

11   Would you keep a secret for one friend if it meant another could get into serious trouble?

12   If a burglar broke into your house and stole just one thing, which one thing would cause the biggest inconvenience?

13   What have you been putting off doing that you should be doing now?

14   Have you ever played a prank on someone that backfired spectacularly?

15   If you could outsource one daily task or chore forever, what would it be?

16   What's your favorite golden oldie song from any decade before you were born?

17   Do you avoid stepping on cracks in the sidewalk? Why?

18   What three "fortunes" would you like to create and place in fortune cookies?

19   If you could switch the lead actors in two movies, what switch would make both movies totally weird?

20   What have you been complimented on most in your life so far?

21 Should a life sentence actually be for life?

22 Which character from a TV show you watched as a kid brings back the happiest memories, and why?

23 In 1919, the Great Molasses Flood killed twenty-one people in Boston. What amazing, interesting, or obscure historical facts do you know?

24 What have you done today that makes you feel proud?

25 Where would you like your memorial bench to be situated once you're gone?

26 If your favorite username was the name of a cologne or perfume, how would it smell?

27 Helen of Troy's face launched a thousand ships. What would you like your face to be able to do?

28 Which actor was (or is) the best James Bond?

29 What have you done that others said you couldn't do?

30 If a drinking glass wasn't called a glass, what name should it be given?

31 Knowing what you know now, if you had to start high school again, what would you do differently?

32 What have you done recently that you should have done a long time ago?

33 Who would you like to sing a duet with? What would you sing?

34 Have you lost contact with someone you wish you could reconnect with? Who is it?

35 What top three hair or beauty essentials could you not live without?

36 Which three colors best describe your personality?

37 If animals could talk, which ones would do the most complaining?

38 What's your favorite Halloween candy?

39 We all know "dad jokes," but what would be a "mom joke"?

40 How many scout knots can you tie?

41   Which tailless animal would be most awesome with a tail?

42   What has been your most embarrassing moment?

43   When you receive a call from a telemarketer, what do you do?

44   If you could change your first name, what name would you choose?

45   When was the last time you swam in the sea?

46   What job has the coolest uniform?

47   Has a chance encounter ever changed the course of your life? What was it?

48   What's the worst thing you've had stuck in your teeth?

49   A box of puppies has been abandoned on your doorstep. What do you do?

50   What one word in the English language would you like to lock in a box before throwing away the key?

51   Would you know what to do if you saw someone choking? Have you ever had to do it?

52   If your child's goldfish died, would you replace it with another and pretend it hadn't?

53   Do you believe there is life more intelligent than humans in the universe?

54   How many of your childhood friends are you still in touch with today?

55   What childhood belief (lost in adulthood) is most special?

56   If you could choose one thing to give as a gift to an unknown newborn baby, what would it be?

57   What makes someone a genius?

58   Your roof has just sprung a leak. What would be the first thing you'd grab to catch the drip?

59   If you could be teleported to any destination in the world, where would it be?

60   What might be a fun alternative to the waiting expression, "until the cows come home"?

61   Have you ever exercised at home with a fitness video? What was the name of the workout?

62   If a fly wasn't called a fly, what would be a more creative name for it?

63   What was the last thing that gave you a static shock?

64   Before Google, where did you find information?

65   What loud noises bother you most?

66   If you could choose the view from your office, what would you like it to be?

67   What three animals would you like to add to a box of animal crackers?

68   If you were a food critic, which restaurant would you like to visit first?

69   What's your favorite font?

70   Have you ever slid down a bannister? When was the last time?

71   How many inflated balloons do you think you could fit in the room you're in now?

72   If you had spare cash to buy something just for fun today, what would you buy?

73   Other than a bath, what was the last thing you dipped your toes into?

74   When was the last time you started a conversation with a stranger?

75   If a movie of your life was made, who should be the director, and why?

76   What movie is overrated?

77   Do you have a special key chain? If so, where did you get it?

78   Which sportsperson could just about everyone around the world name from a picture?

79   What one day in your life would you like to relive?

80   Have you ever been caught telling a lie?

81   When and where did you last see a rainbow?

82   If a snowstorm is a "whiteout," what color of "out" should a rainstorm be?

83   For Gollum it's a ring, but what would you call "my precious"?

84   What's the best outfit you've ever worn to a costume party?

85   You are a thoroughly modern witch. What do you have instead of a broomstick and black cat?

86   Would you have your dominant thumb surgically removed if it meant you'd be immune to all known diseases?

87   In a game of Monopoly, what property do you always try to buy first?

88   You're given $1,000,000 to invest. Where and how do you invest it?

89   What's the best purchase you've made on eBay?

90   Whistles instead of words? What's the most unusual means of communication you've heard of?

91   Where would you go on a dream day out?

92   If you could talk to one animal, what one would it be and why?

93   Under what circumstances would you consider euthanasia for a beloved family pet?

94   What city, state, or country name would make the silliest celebrity baby name?

95   If you could choose your seat on a long-haul jumbo jet flight, where would you sit, and why?

96   What's the craziest thing you've timed yourself doing?

97   Your nose starts to run in public, but you don't have a tissue: what do you do?

98   What's your favorite fairground ride and why?

99   The bridge connecting you to the nearest town is destroyed and you don't have gas to make the detour. What do you do?

100   What's the longest book you've ever read?

101   If you were a genie, but not in a lamp, where would you be and how could you be summoned?

102   What one word would you use to describe your best friend?

103   Should all city centers become traffic-free zones?

104   What was the last thing that happened that made you think you'd dodged a bullet?

105   Have you ever pretended not to be in when someone came to your door? Who was there?

106   We've had Edward Scissorhands, but what else would make good substitutes for hands?

107   What three examples describe your favorite color?

108   If a stranger said they'd pay you $100 for a selfie with you, would you do it?

109   What's the harshest truth you've ever been told?

110   When was the last time you spoke to your neighbors? Do you know their names?

111   Did a teacher ever write anything on your school report that you went on to prove wrong?

112   Which sport should not be classified as a sport?

113   If you had the afternoon off work (or school) at short notice, what would you do with the time?

114   What's the worst thing you've eaten or drunk by mistake thinking it was something else?

115   Which actor is in real life most like the character(s) they play?

116   What makes someone a legend?

117   In a game of Trivial Pursuit, what category is your strongest?

118   If you could go back in time, would you attend college? Why?

119   When you bump into a stranger, what's your first reaction?

120 What's the funniest misspelled tattoo story you've heard?

121 Kangaroos can't move backwards. How would it affect your day if you couldn't?

122 Have you ever drooled in public?

123 If you could choose your siblings, would you have brothers or sisters?

124 Would you give up one year of your own life if it meant your pet could live for another year?

125 What's the craziest sound you've heard a bird imitating?

126 How many gummy bears can you fit into your mouth?

127 If you had time to volunteer for a charity, which one would it be?

128 What's your favorite expression to describe someone who is "not the sharpest tool in the shed"?

129 Do you check people's social media accounts to learn more about them? Who was the last person you checked?

130 What's the biggest favor you've asked someone to do for you?

131 Other than family, do you know anyone who has the same family name as you?

132 If a stray dog followed you home, would you take it in?

133 Before going to sleep tonight, what three things about today will you be most grateful for?

134 You're in a meeting room for a job interview but the interviewer hasn't shown up after thirty minutes. What do you do?

135 What's the best prank you've pulled on someone?

136 You've won an all-expenses-paid trip but you've just sixty seconds to choose a destination. Where would you choose?

137 If you're unhappy with your current weight, what would your ideal weight be?

138 What character from Sesame Street did you (or do you) love the most, and why?

139   Do you have an archnemesis? Who is it?

140   When was the last time you smiled at a stranger?

141   60s, 70s, 80s, 90s, 00s, 10s: Which decade did you love the most and why?

142   In a movie of your life, what soundtrack would convey the mood of today's events?

143   How many high school sweethearts do you know who got married and stayed together?

144   What's guaranteed to give you gas or indigestion?

145   Have you ever played Dungeons and Dragons?

146   What was the last molehill that you made into a mountain?

147   If a time-traveler from fifty years ago arrived in the world today, what would disappoint them?

148   When and why do you like to be alone?

149   What's a good example of "just because it's popular doesn't mean it's good"?

150   On a scale of one to ten (with ten the healthiest), how healthy is your diet?

151   We've had generations X, Y, and Z; what generation is next?

152   If a year of your life could be traded for $25,000, how many years would you trade in?

153   Which six people would you want to be stranded on a deserted island with, and why?

154   Have you ever snuck into anywhere without paying?

155   If aliens landed, where would you take them first on a whistle-stop tour of life on Earth?

156   How many male-female singing duos can you name?

157   What three foods would taste better if they were dipped in chocolate?

158   You are an indestructible cartoon character and are falling from an airplane without a parachute. What will happen next?

159   What's your favorite expression that describes feeling very tired?

160   Would you give a hitchhiker a ride?

161   What would you like your spirit animal to be?

162   If you could snap your fingers and be any height, would you choose to become taller or shorter?

163   Do you always walk around supermarket aisles in the same order?

164   What childhood award or prize are you most proud of winning?

165   A hundred years from now, how would you like to be remembered?

166   Who deserves the title of "biggest sports cheat"?

167   Which actor would be the most ridiculous choice for the role of Indiana Jones?

168   If you had to answer questions on your specialist subject, what would the subject be?

169   What makes someone a nerd?

170   Have you ever been disappointed by a hotel room that looked nothing like the brochure?

171   What would you do if you saw a colleague steal something from your workplace?

172   When was the last time you shared a bath with someone?

173   Under what circumstances would you say it's better to be safe than sorry?

174   What one word yelled in a public place would cause the most chaos?

175   If you're waiting for your ship to come in, what's on that ship?

176   What's the last thing you do before you go to sleep at night?

177   You've won a two-week cruise for two. Who would you take with you?

178   What would happen if everyone on Earth jumped at the same time?

179   Do you know what every button on your TV remote control is for?

180   Which shade of beige is your favorite, and what creative name can you give it?

181   What would be a good name for a fifth musketeer?

182   If you had to arm wrestle the person sitting closest to you now, would you win?

183   What's the most irksome challenge you deal with in daily life?

184   Where would you absolutely refuse to go alone?

185   The Japanese have a word for gathering books that you're unlikely to ever read. What word would you use?

186   If all but one Christmas song should be banned, which one should be kept?

187   Have you ever spoken up for someone else? What was it about?

188   What will you do for your pets that you will not do for other family members?

189   Other than having a cold, what makes you sneeze?

190   What was the last item you put in your basket on Amazon?

191   If you could create a new martial art, what would you call it?

192   What's your favorite Elvis song? If you don't have one, why not?

193   Should breakdancing be an Olympic sport?

194   Hippocampus hippocampus is a seahorse. What's the weirdest scientific name for something you know?

195   What were you doing the last time you questioned your sanity?

196   If you had to attach a "most likely to..." to three of your friends, what would they be?

197   Knowledge is power: what do you wish you were more knowledgeable about?

198   What's the worst thing that's happened to you in a fitting room?

199   If you were a ghost, who would you haunt for fun?

200   What things should you pay more attention to than you do?

201   In a parallel universe, what might be going on in Area 51?

202   Would you ever consider shaving your hair off to raise money for charity?

203   Do you avoid walking under ladders? Why?

204   What three foodstuffs are must-haves in a picnic?

205   If all jobs paid the same salary, would you change your career?

206   What's the most ridiculous way you've managed to injure yourself?

207   Have you ever squeezed a pimple on someone else's body?

208   What's the scariest storm you've been in?

209   When was the last time you screamed out loud, and why?

210   The immortal hero in your novel can only be killed by one thing. What everyday thing is it?

211   What task would you least like to have to do alone?

212   Have you visited a national park? Which one(s)?

213   What's your preferred backup option for data? Why?

214   What characters might Alice in Wonderland have met in a parallel universe?

215   When did you first feel like a grown-up and what were you doing?

216   If you could customize your car, what would you add?

217   Do you believe that no one is indispensable in the workplace?

218   What sound would you least like to hear if you were home alone at night?

219   Have you ever slept in a sleeping bag? When was the last time?

220   What smells make you gag?

221   If you were a giant garden gnome, what pose would you be in?

222   Which Scooby-Doo character are you most like?

223 What score out of ten would your friends give you as a dancer?

224 How many of your Facebook friends are people you physically spend time with regularly?

225 What one item do you always carry with you "just in case"?

226 You've turned into the main character in the last TV show you watched. Who are you?

227 What's your favorite Disney movie? If you don't have one, why not?

228 If you had to be a leader of something, what would it be?

229 What's your preferred non-dairy milk alternative?

230 If you could only choose one pie for Thanksgiving, sweet or savory, what would it be?

231 We've had laptops and palmtops, so what should we have next?

232 Is it possible to forgive and forget?

233 If all the countries became one united country, what city would become Earth's capital?

234 What's the hardest physical work you've ever done?

235 Would you eat squirrel meat? Have you tried it?

236 Which prize would you choose: a $200,000 luxury car or $200,000 cash?

237 How many hours of TV do you watch in a typical week?

238 Have you ever dressed in the national costume of another country? Which one?

239 If your best friend was granted three wishes, what do you think they would be?

240 What's the highest calorie food you could carry with you to fuel a two-day mountain hike?

241 How much money would entice you to gain a hundred pounds and keep it on for at least one year?

242 Which optional herbs or spices do you always leave out of a recipe and why?

243 What's the ickiest thing you've ever accidentally sat on?

244 You are blindfolded and must visit the place you pin on a map. Where would you hope not to pin?

245 What was the last new word you learned?

246 If you could design a coat of arms for your family, what symbols would you include?

247 What's the most amazing thing you've seen in a slow-motion video?

248 Which actors have become typecast?

249 What makes the best breakfast ever?

250 If you had to be an insect, which one would you be, and why?

251 What's the worst thing you could be wearing if you were rushed to the ER?

252 How many people do you follow on social media?

253 What new flavor of cotton candy would you like to create?

254 When was the last time you sat on a teeter-totter/seesaw?

255 What's the strangest cultural tradition you've learned of?

256 If all the lights in your home and street suddenly went out at night, what would you do?

257 Do you ever accept second best?

258 What three ingredients do you need to make a great-tasting smoothie?

259 Other than KFC, what else is finger lickin' good?

260 What music festival would you most like to go to?

261 If you were a high-dive champion, what new dive move would you invent and what would you call it?

262 Which sci-fi movie best predicts the future of life on Earth?

263   What modern gadget would make a great steampunk creation?

264   Who did you last play frisbee with, and where?

265   What's your favorite cookie to have with milk?

266   If all your thoughts so far today appeared as text above your head, how many people would you have offended already?

267   What memory of you as a kid does your family like to embarrass you with by telling everyone?

268   Have you ever experienced a deafening silence?

269   What's the last thing you do before leaving your home to go away for a few days?

270   If your birthday could be on a different date, which one would you choose, and why?

271   What childhood toy do you still have today?

272   Using your MacGyver-like skills, what could you use to escape from a flooded underground tunnel?

273   Helen Back? Ben Dover? What unfortunate and funny name combinations have you heard of?

274   Would you eat packaged food that's passed its expiration date?

275   You've spilled red wine on a white carpet: what do you do?

276   If you could do one magic spell, what word would you say as you waved your wand?

277   We've had Snakes on a Plane, so what would you like to put on a plane next?

278   The last meal you ate will become an art installation. What will you call it?

279   What inanimate object have you seen a face in? Was it a famous face?

280   In a twenty-first-century revamp, what new names should be given to Velma, Daphne, and Fred in Scooby-Doo?

281   Did the tooth fairy visit your home when you were little?

282   What has happened in your life that you never thought would?

283   When was the last time you sat in silence?

284   If Alvin the chipmunk wasn't called Alvin, what name should he have?

285   If you had to be without one sense (sight, sound, taste, touch, smell) for a day, which would you choose?

286   What game for one player do you like to play?

287   Have you ever sneaked a peek at someone else's journal?

288   What was the last picture you took that wasn't a selfie?

289   If you could master any skill or talent, what would it be?

290   Have you ever played a piñata game and what's your best piñata story?

291   Should all things Christmas be illegal until December first?

292   What's the most annoying thing you've forgotten to do more than once?

293   How many people do you hug in an average day?

294   If an orange didn't share its name with its color, what would you call it?

295   Do you ever drink iced coffee or tea in the winter?

296   What's your favorite Clint Eastwood movie? If you don't have one, why not?

297   If you were a landscape artist, what landscape would you most want to paint?

298   What's the most awesome thing you've known people be able to do with their feet in place of their hands?

299   Which room in your home do you spend the most time in?

300   Like February 29th, what other day do you wish only came around every four years instead of every year?

301   What three performers (alive or dead) would you like to see perform together on stage?

302   If you could earn a PhD in the subject you happen to know most about right now, what would it be in?

303 What food looks way better than it tastes?

304 Have you ever pretended a store-bought cake was homemade?

305 Remember soap on a rope? What new thing would you market on a rope?

306 What facial expression do you have that speaks volumes without you saying a word?

307 If your first name was an acronym, what would the letters stand for?

308 Where would be the worst place to have a heart attack?

309 What color do you most associate with holidays?

310 Have you ever stockpiled food or household items in case of shortage?

311 What other colors would you like pandas to come in?

312 If you had to build something that could be seen from space, what would you create?

313 What food should always be bought fresh, not canned or frozen?

314 Do you believe anything is possible and nothing is impossible? If not, why not?

315 Would you eat a beetle on a dare?

316 In a twenty-first-century version of Hansel and Gretel, what might they leave a trail with instead of breadcrumbs?

317 What ingredients make the best ice cream float?

318 Have you ever been heartbroken? What happened?

319 What habit is the most annoying?

320 When was the last time you said, "Why me?" and what prompted it?

321 You've only thirty seconds to recite the alphabet backward or the fluffy bunny gets it. Could you do it?

322 What's the most creative excuse for being late you could invent and get away with?

323 Can long-distance relationships work?

324   If you could eat your plates instead of washing them, what would you want them to taste like?

325   You arrive at work and realize you've forgotten your packed lunch. What do you do at lunchtime?

326   What color has gone out of fashion most recently? Are you still wearing it?

327   Other than lemonade, what's the best thing you can make with lemons?

328   What's your least favorite Christmas carol?

329   If you had to compete for your country in a sport tomorrow, which one would you do best (or least bad) in?

330   What have you argued for in the past that really doesn't matter to you anymore?

331   Which ravioli filling is your favorite?

332   What's the sound of summer?

333   Has a small act of kindness ever had a big impact on you?

334   What was the last question you asked your smart speaker?

335   What are your favorite items to purchase from a farmers market?

336   What job is the ideal first job for teenagers?

337   If asked to describe your day so far in three words, what would you say?

338   Hippos wallow in mud. What would you most like to wallow in?

339   A TV network wants to interview you for a feature about your employer. What do you do?

340   What's the most creative thing you could make with an old newspaper?

341   Who do you count on the most for help?

342   Which ancient monument would be the saddest loss to the world if it crumbled to dust?

343   If you were a news anchor, what breaking news story would you most like to read out?

344 What might be an alternative ending to the story of *Little Red Riding Hood*?

345 Do you believe in angels? Have you seen one?

346 What's the worst thing that could be made into "leftovers pie"?

347 If your friends had to give you a nickname that summed up your attitude, what would it be?

348 What movie prop would you most like to own?

349 Have you ever eaten so much that you had to lie down to ease the discomfort? When was the last time?

350 What three reasons do you have to be cheerful today?

351 How many people do you know with the same first name as you?

352 When was the last time you said, "That's cool!"?

353 What mythical beast would you most like to be real?

354 Visitors to your town want to know a good place to eat. Where would you send them?

355 Would you eat food you didn't recognize without asking what it was? Have you done that?

356 What's the strangest cult you've heard of?

357 If you had to convey your anger without making a sound, how would you do it?

358 Are all the clocks in your home twenty-four-hour digital clocks?

359 Have you ever struggled to do something that was promoted as "idiot-proof"? What was it?

360 What's your favorite cake frosting?

361 When did you last "party like it's 1999"?

362 What's the smallest thing you've seen in nature?

363 You've invented a new super-strength industrial adhesive. What will you call it?

364 What might Butch Cassidy and the Sundance Kid be called in a parallel universe?

365 If you could flip a switch and a household chore would be done, which chore would you want it to be?

366 What smells do you find relaxing?

367 The number of weddings and funerals you've been to becomes the title of a movie. What's the title?

368 What children's story character used to scare you when you were a child?

369 In a twenty-first-century update, what items might your true love receive over the twelve days of Christmas?

370 Which radio station do you listen to most often?

371 What pet names do you have (or have had) for private body parts?

372 For how long would you give chase if your umbrella got taken out of your hand by the wind?

373 How many fries would make a fair trade for a chicken nugget?

374 What older celebrity looks better now than they did when they were younger?

375 If baboons didn't have blue bottoms, what color would make a fabulous alternative?

376 Have you ever struggled to open "easy open" packaging?

377 What was the last thing that made you itch?

378 If you had to compile a top ten list of your favorite pies, which one would get the number one spot?

379 What makes the best wedding outfit?

380 Do you believe that everyone has a look-alike somewhere in the world? Have you met any?

What other words do you use for a "thingamajig"?

Should ancient human remains displayed in museums be returned to their homeland?

383   If bubble gum was savory, what flavor would you like it to be?

384   What's the saddest headstone or grave marker you've ever seen?

385   When was the last time you said, "That sucks!"? Why?

386   What's the weirdest sport you've played?

387   If you had to delete all but three pictures from your phone, which three would you keep?

388   What three songs are you most likely to sing in the shower?

389   Do you listen to podcasts? What have you listened to most recently?

390   What songs are on your "let's get this done" soundtrack?

391   Would you describe yourself as a hard worker, and what are you working hard on now?

392   What's your favorite Bruce Springsteen song? If you don't have one, why not?

393   If you were a pirate captain, what would you name your ship?

394   What subject taught in school have you used most in life outside school?

395   Other than money, what else do you wish grew on trees?

396   Where would be the most annoying place to have a boil?

397   What's the strangest phobia you've ever heard of?

398   If Buddy Holly had survived the plane crash, what might the title of his next hit song have been?

399   What thing that your parents always warned you about turned out to be good advice?

400   You can have an unlimited supply of one type of candy for the rest of your life. What will you choose?

401   What's the worst thing that could happen while you're brushing your teeth?

402   If you could gain a qualification today, what would you like it to be?

403   Have you ever wished you were older?

404   What color of car do you least like?

405   You've invented a new energy source. What is it and what will you name it?

406   What's the silliest thing you've cried over recently?

407   Like Sleeping Beauty, you've fallen into a hundred-year sleep; what will change most in the world before you wake up?

408   What were the choices the last time you had to flip a coin?

409   Do you ever give up on reading a book when you're already halfway through?

410   Which popular movie needs a different title, and what title would you give it?

411   If your friends had to meet you in a bookstore, in what section would they look for you?

412   What's the one thing you don't want people to say when you've just broken up with someone?

413   Which animal is the deadliest in the world?

414   ModelLand has opened in California. What theme park would you like to open?

415   If cartoon characters had rap careers, who would be the best?

416   What will Earth look like ten thousand years from now?

417   Who do you find it difficult to feel sorry for?

418   Have you ever tidied up a room by stuffing everything into a closet?

419   When was the last time you said, "Bring it on!" and why?

420   What would be a funny message to paint on the underside of your boat?

421   Cat-opoly? What make-your-own-opoly board would you create?

422   Have you ever experienced buyer's remorse? If so, what was the purchase?

423   What would be the most inappropriate drive-thru?

424   If you could get a shopping cart full of food and drink for free, what would you put in it?

425　What's the most unusual thing you've ever used as a bookmark?

426　When did you last behave selfishly? How?

427　Mr. Baker the baker? What's the funniest example of a person's name fitting their job?

428　What's your favorite brand of gum and why?

429　If you were a salad, what type of dressing would be the best match for you?

430　What was the last thing that made you laugh out loud?

431　Do you have an item of jewelry that you never take off? What is it?

432　What "buy one get one free" would be of absolutely no use to you?

433　On a scale of one to ten, how embarrassing is your passport photo?

434　What's the oddest thing you've ever seen in a museum?

435　Would you dance differently if you thought no one was watching?

436　If cats came in every color, would you choose one that matched your home décor?

437　What would you do if you had to poop in someone else's house and it wouldn't flush?

438　Have you ever toasted marshmallows on an open fire? When was the last time?

439　The Olympics are coming to your hometown and you need to design a mascot. What will it be?

440　A home makeover show decorates your bedroom: what's the worst color scheme they could use?

441　In what decade would you most like to have been a teenager?

442　What color Power Ranger would you be?

443　How many European capital cities can you name?

444　Which pop princess would make the most ridiculous lead singer in a heavy metal band?

445   What would you like to take lessons in?

446   If you had to describe your personality as a smell, what would it be?

447   What one stupid thing you did as a teenager are you most embarrassed by now?

448   You've invented a new board game. What are your playing pieces?

449   What three songs have been on your playlist for the longest time?

450   Other than playing table tennis, what are two other uses for a table tennis ball?

451   If *Charlie's Angels* was remade with an all-male cast, who should play the lead roles?

452   What makes the difference between living and existing?

453   Have you ever experienced déjà vu?

454   What would your team name be if you and your friends went bowling?

455   If cobwebs were colorful, would you still dust them away?

456   What's the oldest thing in nature you've seen?

457   When was the last time you put on a brave face but were dying inside?

458   Where were you shopping and what were you buying when you last experienced excellent customer service?

459   If you could get free season tickets for any team in any sport, what would you get?

460   What's your favorite board game?

461   Do you ever keep your New Year's resolutions?

462   Would you consider being frozen (cryogenics) and brought back to life in the future?

463   How many people do you know (personally) with a name that begins with B?

464   What's the best bargain you've picked up in a sale?

465   If cockroaches could talk, what would they say and sound like?

466   What's the worst parking you've seen, and where was it?

467   You can only eat one type of bread for the rest of your life. What type will you choose?

468   What's been the easiest money you've ever made?

469   If you could give anyone a radio shout-out right now, who would it be?

470   What's the strangest room you've ever been in, and why were you there?

471   Should animals have the same rights as humans?

472   In a twenty-first-century version of the *Wizard of Oz*, what might Dorothy wear instead of ruby-red shoes?

473   What was the last thing that made you say, "Wow!"?

474   Which planet in our solar system would you most like to visit?

475   What's the oddest thing you keep in the trunk of your car?

476   Have you ever been in a burping contest, and did you win?

477   What's the best optical illusion you've ever seen?

478   If dinosaurs were reintroduced, where in the world today would be their ideal habitat?

479   Can you remember the words to the children's song *"Frère Jacques"*?

480   In what general knowledge quiz category is your knowledge generally not that great?

481   What's the best way to recover after being left hanging for a high-five?

482   Have you ever been convinced someone was telling you a lie and it turned out to be true? What was it?

483   What color would make a black hole more inviting?

484   How many gadgets do you have at home that beep at you?

485   What's the most wasteful thing that you do?

486 If you had to describe your week so far through the medium of dance, what dance would it be?

487 Which app on your phone is the most useful, and which is the most useless but fun?

488 If your goal is world dominance, what's your first step?

489 What's the most useless superhero power?

490 You've invented a fastener to take over in place of Velcro (hook and loop): what is it?

491 What's your favorite ABBA song and do you know all the lyrics?

492 When did you last eat alphabet pasta and what words did you create?

493 If you could get ten tickets to anything you wanted, what would you choose and who would you bring?

494 What three things are essential in making a dream treehouse?

495 Have you ever stood in a long, long line to buy something? What was it?

496 When was the last time you pushed a door labeled "pull"?

497 What's the coolest website you've stumbled upon that no one seems to know about?

498 If your hair could be any color for one day, what would it be?

499 Who do you know that has been married the longest? How many years?

500 Would you burn McDonald's burger-scented candles in your home?

501 If Elvis was still alive today, what would he be wearing?

502 What's the funniest thing you've heard a child innocently blurt out?

503 Mashed potato? Twist? What old-school dance moves do you know?

504 What's the funniest super glue incident you've heard of?

505 Do you believe that a full moon can affect people's behavior? Why?

506 What's the greatest threat to humanity?

507 Hot Dog High is an actual place: do you know anyone who has applied to drive a "wienermobile"?

508 In what location would you most like to sleep under the stars?

509 Have you ever been in a food fight?

510 What's the oddest sight you've ever seen?

511 If you were a spy, what would your code name be?

512 Other than the sun, what's the hottest thing you've seen in nature?

513 What "did you know?" fact do you keep at the ready to get a conversation started?

514 Monday morning blues? What new word can you come up with to describe that Monday morning feeling?

515 Given the choice, what color and design of front door would you have?

516 What one song would you like the whole world to be able to sing?

517 Have you ever done something just to impress someone else? What was it?

518 What's the worst tattoo you've ever seen on someone?

519 Where were you and what were you doing the last time you felt totally relaxed?

520 What's the laziest thing you've ever done?

521 The paparazzi mistake you for someone famous and surround you with cameras: which celebrity is it and what do you do?

522 What color would the big red button need to be to make you less inclined to push it?

523 Not housewife, domestic goddess. What's the best description you can come up with for the most mundane job?

524 What was the last thing that really grabbed your attention?

525 Are you happy when you're alone?

526 What's the most dangerous job or career?

527   Which part of your body has the highest value for insurance purposes?

528   What's the most unusual or odd-shaped building you've been in?

529   If you could go back in time to see a brand-new invention being unveiled, where would you go?

530   What three things are you good at?

531   You've fallen at home and can't get up. Would you drink from the dog's bowl to avoid dehydration?

532   What's the funniest thing you've overheard?

533   When was the last time you polished your shoes?

534   What's your favorite "until you're blue in the face" expression?

535   On a scale of one to ten, how good would you say your handwriting is?

536   What makes the ideal workout?

537   How many people in your family can curl their tongue and are you one of them?

538   What's the funniest cheesy country song title you've ever heard?

539   Would you be happy to travel in a driverless car?

540   If you had to display a full suit of armor in your home, where would you position it?

541   What's the most fun thing you've ever found inside a Christmas cracker?

542   Have you ever fallen asleep somewhere you shouldn't have? Where was it?

543   Do you catch the news every day? What headline caught your eye today?

544   What's the funniest pet cat name you've ever heard?

545   You can only have one type of flooring in your home: what will you choose?

546   Have you ever told ghost stories around a campfire and what were they?

547   What's the most politically incorrect thing you've said or done recently?

548 Could you explain in three steps how to make a cup of tea to someone who has never done it?

549 Which one of your senses would you most like to have magnified to super-strength?

550 Have you ever farted in a jar to keep it as a pet?

551 If you had to draw a picture right now, what would you be most likely to draw?

552 What's the most ridiculous warning sign you've ever seen?

553 How many foods can you name that begin with the letter R?

554 When did you last feel bored?

555 If you were a squirrel, where would you hide your nuts to stop others stealing them?

556 What's your all-time favorite dip?

557 Should athletes be allowed to use performance-enhancing technology?

558 What's your favorite "just add water" thing?

559 In what one way do you feel you differ most from your parents?

560 What crazy fitness trend would you like to start?

561 Do you ever push harder and harder on the remote-control buttons, even though the battery is dead?

562 What's your best "why did the chicken cross the road" joke?

563 When was the last time you performed a random act of kindness and what was it?

564 What's the most unusual animal you've held in your hands or touched?

565 If your hands were tied behind your back, could you get your socks on?

566 Who do you know that you would describe as a "character" and why?

567 What was the last thing to make you face palm?

568   Have you ever been in a situation where you just didn't know what to say? What happened?

569   What's the one thing that you and your friends can never agree on?

570   If you could go on a dinner date with anyone (dead or alive) tonight, who would it be?

571   What's the most unlikely thing to hear a news anchor say?

572   Other than Uncle Buck, do you know anyone who microwaves their socks?

573   What's the most ridiculous thing you could stuff a mattress with?

574   How many people would you share a password with?

575   If ethics weren't an issue, what mad scientist experiment would you like to trial on humans?

576   You've discovered the secret to eternal youth: what is it?

577   What's the most outdated expression you still regularly use?

578   Goat yoga? What's the weirdest type of yoga you've heard of or tried?

579   If your index fingers suddenly doubled in length, how would it affect your day?

580   What's the funniest home video you've ever seen?

581   Would you allow two elderly adults to die if it meant one child would be saved?

582   What's the most sexist thing anyone has ever said to you?

583   On a scale of one to ten, how much do you like pumpkin pie?

584   Where were you and what were you doing the last time you felt nervous walking into a building?

585   If you could have a famous band play at your funeral, who would it be?

586   What three things are you most grateful for in your life?

587   Have you ever pretended to be an answerphone message?

588   What "pick and mix" or penny candy items do you always pick first?

589   If you had to describe yourself as a book genre, what would it be?

590   What other colors would you like white fluffy clouds to come in?

591   Did you bounce on the bed when you were a kid?

592   What's the most unbelievable thing you've ever heard someone say?

593   Which one of your relatives is most likely to embarrass you at a family gathering?

594   If everything you ate tasted the same, would you still eat a variety of foods?

595   Do you have a secret hunch about how you will die?

596   Have you ever been lost in a maze?

597   What's the most exciting thing you've ever found in the least exciting place?

598   Do you ever read the last page of a book before getting to the end?

599   What's the most tedious part of an average day for you?

600   If given the opportunity, would you do a parachute jump?

601   When was the last time you owed someone money?

602   The person you're standing next to on a crowded train has bad body odor. What do you do?

603   What creative use can you come up with for a single glove?

604   In what way would your life be better if you had x-ray vision?

605   What makes the most satisfying sound?

606   How many pieces were there in the biggest jigsaw you ever completed?

607   What's the most stupid cause of accidental death you've heard of?

608   Would getting rid of "likes" on social media help reduce anxiety?

609   Have you ever felt like a big fish in a small pond? When?

610   What's the worst gift you've ever received?

611   Do you celebrate Thanksgiving, and what's at the center of your celebrations?

612   What common occurrence in movies rarely happens in real life?

613   If grass wasn't green, what color would you like it to be?

614   You can only keep one electrical appliance in your kitchen: which one will you choose?

615   What's the funniest explanation of how babies are made that you've heard?

616   How many pink things can you list in the next ten seconds?

617   What's the longest distance you've ever jogged?

618   If you were a storm chaser, what type of storm would you most like to chase?

619   What was the last thing to make your fingers sticky?

620   Have you ever been on a blind date?

621   What's the first thought that goes through your mind when you see a homeless person?

622   If you could have a home in a different country, where would it be?

623   What alternative uses have you found for a handkerchief?

624   When did you last jump in a puddle?

625   You've developed a new brand of cat food. What's its name?

626   What's your biggest worry right now?

627   Do you like marmalade sandwiches as much as Paddington Bear does?

628   What's the craziest gadget you've seen advertised on a teleshopping channel?

629   Have you ever pretended not to know something? What was it?

630   With what items do you always go for quantity over quality?

631   If gravity suddenly didn't exist, what would you hit on the way up from where you are right now?

632   What three things are you most looking forward to this year?

633   If your initials are the name of a new deadly virus, what would the name be and the symptoms?

634   What's the best thing you've found down the back of your sofa?

635   Other than water, what would you most like to jump into a pool of?

636   When was the last time you made yourself dizzy?

637   What's one useless general fact or nugget of trivia you know?

638   How many rooms are in your dream house, and what are they all for?

639   If you had to eat a crayon, what color would you choose?

640   Do you listen to any music today that your parents listened to when they were your age?

641   What's the most ridiculous rule you've ever had to follow?

642   If Greyhound Lines hadn't chosen the greyhound, what would make a great bus logo?

643   Who do you know who can never keep a secret?

644   What's the dumbest way you've heard of a criminal being caught?

645   If you could have a life-sized model of any animal in your home, what would you have?

646   Which one of your friends is most likely to invent something useful?

647   Where were you and what were you doing on the hottest day you can remember?

648   If you were a superhero by night, what day job would you have to protect your identity?

649   Which bit of a trifle is the best?

650   Should bands stop going on world tours to help save the environment?

651   What's a good name for a fear of hot dogs?

652   Have you ever been on a Ferris wheel? What could you see from the top?

653   What crime is the most evil of all?

654   If humans became caged exhibits in zoos, what habitat would they be housed in?

655   What is the most adventurous outdoor activity you would attempt?

656   Has anyone ever accused you of being the Grinch? Why?

657   What would you most like to be the leader of?

658   If you had to eat dessert for breakfast, what would you have?

659   What was the last thing you asked Santa Claus to bring you?

660   Easier said than done? What do you find easy in theory but difficult in practice?

661   What's the worst lie you've ever told?

662   If your kettle could speak, what would it say as it boils?

663   What would you do if you found twenty dollars in a hotel room drawer?

664   Do you name your car, and what other objects in your life have you named?

665   What's your best waterslide story?

666   Would you allow an animal to die to save a person?

667   Instead of "one small step . . ." what would be a funny alternative Neil Armstrong moon-landing quote?

668   What would be the worst thing you could say on a first date?

669   Have you ever tried to burp the alphabet? How far did you get?

670   What makes the perfect pop song?

671   Do you care what other people think about you?

672   What's the most ridiculous reason for a couple breaking up that you've heard of?

673   If your life depended on leaping across an eight-foot gap between high rooftops, would you attempt it?

674   Which accent do you find sexiest?

675   A spoon and fork combo is a *spork*. What other utensil combo could you create and what would you call it?

676   When was the last time you made someone a cup of tea?

677   You've cultivated a new type of vegetable. What is it and what do you call it?

678   What would be the hardest thing about living in a lighthouse?

679   If you had to fake your own death, how would you do it?

680   What's the dumbest reason for going to the ER you've heard of?

681   Which one of your friends or family has the neatest handwriting?

682   Have you ever tried to check if the light goes off when you close the fridge door?

683   What would be a great name for a new gym?

684   Do you have an old pair of socks that you can't bear to part with?

685   What word starts to sound weird the more you say it?

686   Have you ever tried to lick your elbow?

687   What's the most ridiculous celebrity baby name you've heard?

688   If you could have a private cookery lesson with a chef, which cuisine would you choose?

689   Winnie-the-Pooh needs a makeover. How will you dress him?

690   What was wrong with you the last time you were ill?

691   On a scale of one to ten, how reliable would your friends say you are, and why?

692   What crossword cryptic clue are you most proud of solving?

693   The picnic you planned is rained out. What do you do instead?

694   What three things around you right now could you use to make a musical instrument?

695   If you were a supervillain, what would your name be?

696   Are there are more good than bad people in the world?

697   What's your best vacation disaster story?

698   Have you ever tried to run up a down escalator?

699   What's the craziest vehicle you've ever seen on a highway?

700   When did you last play leapfrog, and could you still do it today?

701   You can only stockpile one item in preparation for potential home confinement. What is it?

702   What things do you do without realizing you did them, or without remembering you did them?

703   Which one of your friends or family members is scariest when they're angry?

704   Other than when you're sick, have you ever spent an entire day in bed? When was the last time?

705   What's one thing you've had to unlearn?

706   If you had to draw your life as a line, what would it look like?

707   What Starburst flavor is your absolute favorite?

708   Do you walk your talk?

709   What's the most ridiculous outfit you've seen paraded on a catwalk?

710   When was the last time you jumped rope, and can you remember any rhymes?

711   Instead of a white flag, what should be waved to signify surrender?

712   Which appliance in your home is the noisiest when in use?

713   if you could have afternoon tea with a world leader, who would it be?

714   What song or piece of music would you be glad never to hear again?

715   Did you play a cootie game in school, and who did you think had cooties?

716   What was the last thing you ate that made you extremely thirsty?

717   Will you ever be happier than you are right now?

718   How many email addresses do you have, and which is your favorite?

719   What should the punishment be for people who don't return supermarket carts properly?

720   If your nose had to be a fruit, what fruit would you want it to be?

721   Have you ever tried to sneeze with your eyes open?

722   Do you have an outdated tech item that you don't want to upgrade? What is it?

723   What pajamas did you love the most when you were younger?

724   Have you ever been so desperate to pee that you thought your bladder might burst?

725   What's the deepest underground you've been?

726   You've created a new search engine: what will you call it?

727   What pair of shoes have you loved the most in your life so far?

728   How cold is too cold?

729   What new language would you like to be fluent in, and why?

730   Instead of piggy in the middle (or monkey in the middle), what might be in the middle in a parallel universe?

731   What's your best travel sickness story?

732   Do you notice other people's spelling and grammar errors more than your own?

733   What culture in another country would you find it most difficult to adopt?

734   Who do you know who could be described as the "salt of the earth"?

735   Have you ever trimmed a friend's hair? Would you, if they asked?

736   If you had to exchange ears with an animal, which one would you choose?

737   What mnemonic has helped you most?

738   Granny? Grandma? What names do you give your grandparents?

739   What makes the perfect topping for frozen yogurt?

740   If you were a three-course meal, what dishes would you be?

741   What three things could go missing from your home and you might never notice?

742   Have you ever done a bad thing that turned out to be a good thing? What was it?

743   Should fossil fuels be banned?

744   What magic trick would you most like to be able to perform?

745   Are you the most competitive person you know, and if not, who is?

746   Where is the weirdest place you've found a missing TV remote control?

747   What have you done after being double dared to do it?

748   Will there ever be a world without hunger?

749   What's the craziest thing you've seen someone balance on their head?

750   If your only weapon in a zombie apocalypse is whatever you can reach right now, would you survive?

751   What food should be made available as a spread?

752   When was the last time you jumped into a pile of raked leaves?

753   What pattern would make the funniest crop circle when viewed from the air?

754   Have you ever felt addicted to playing a game? Which one?

755   What film from the last year should get the Golden Raspberry Award (for worst film)?

756   Did you or do you still have a CD collection? What was the last CD you bought?

757   What's the worst case of medical malpractice you've heard of?

758   If you could have any style of designer sunglasses, what would you choose?

759   If it didn't rain cats and dogs, what should it rain?

760   Have you ever pretended to understand something that you really didn't? What was it?

761   What accessories are needed to make a perfect snowman?

762   There are three crocodiles between you and a $1 million dollar prize. What do you do?

763   What's the most random thing you've ever found in one of your pockets?

764   Which one of your friends or family members would be the best at belly dancing?

765   Do you believe in Bigfoot?

766   What was the last thing you beat yourself up about?

767   If you had to fly south for winter, where would you go?

768   What's your best tip for dealing with stinky sneakers?

769   Other than your birthday, what day of the year is your favorite, and why?

770   What would you like your last words to be?

771   Instead of a zillion or gazillion, what name can you invent for a huge number?

772   What's the most profound thing anyone has ever said to you?

773   You've created a new mocktail. What's in it and what have you called it?

774   What's the craziest thing you've thrown across a room in a temper?

775   Will the world ever know who Banksy is?

776   What's a good example of a product creating a solution and then looking for the problem?

777   If your pants really did catch fire when you lie, would your butt have been scorched today?

778   Have you ever felt like you wanted to swing from the chandeliers? Why?

779   When did you last ride a bike?

780   If it wasn't called a "Hershey's Kiss," what name would you give it?

781   Which bit of astronaut training would you do best in?

782   If you had to give a twenty-minute presentation tomorrow, what would you talk about?

783   What YouTuber do you watch most?

784   On a scale of one to ten, with ten being the weirdest, how weird would you say you are?

785   *Boing,* buzz, *splash* . . . What's your favorite onomatopoeic word?

786   What would your cowboy name be?

787   When was the last time you joined a conga line and where?

788   If you could have anything delivered to you right now, what would it be?

789   You discover an unknown species of plant. What does it look like and what will you name it?

790   What would you say is pure bliss?

791   Which one of your friends would be most likely to win a plate-spinning contest?

792   What three things do adults have that children want to have?

793   Instead of the well-known *"bong,"* what sound would be a fun chime for Big Ben?

794   If you were a Transformer, what vehicle would you be when you transformed?

795   What's a healthy way to let off steam and vent frustration?

796   How many emotions can you convey using facial expressions and gestures alone?

797   What current trend do you just not get?

798   The record for holding the plank position is over eight hours. How long can you hold it?

799   What period of history would you like to visit for a day?

800   If it's your job to hire and fire, how do you fire someone who is also a friend?

801   What's your best tip for dealing with a cramp?

802   Have you ever tripped over your own shoelaces? What happened next?

803   What's the best voicemail message you've heard?

804   Do you have any compulsive behaviors?

805   Will the internet break one day? What will cause it?

806   If you could have just one piece of home exercise equipment, what would it be?

807   Have you ever put anyone on a pedestal? If so, who and are they still there?

808   If Italy is boot-shaped, what shape can be used to describe your country?

809   What's the worst diet you've ever gone on?

810   Have you ever had braces and what did you do to celebrate on the day they were removed?

811   What makes the perfect topping for Shredded Wheat?

812   If your pets (past and present) had to give you a reference for a job, would you get the position?

813   What was the last thing you bought for a secret Santa gift?

814   Have you ever twerked?

815   What's the craziest thing you can imagine discovering at the center of the Earth?

816   Will the world become free of single-use plastics in your lifetime?

817   What's the craziest thing you've balanced on to help you reach something high?

818   "Death by chocolate" is a popular dessert. What other foods should carry a "danger of death" warning?

819   Where's the most embarrassing place your stomach has growled?

820   Is "having a blonde moment" an offensive expression? Why?

821   What's the funniest place name you've ever seen?

822   When was the last time you heard birds singing and where were you?

823   You've created a new carpet shampoo. What does it smell of and what do you name it?

824   What's the best word you've ever made in a game of Scrabble?

825   Who do you know who has mastered the art of eating all they can at an all-you-can-eat buffet?

826   What's the most painful thing you've ever stepped on without shoes?

827   How common is common sense?

828   What current world news event would you find most difficult to explain to a seven-year-old child?

829   If James Bond didn't drink martinis, "shaken not stirred," what drink would be the most hilarious alternative?

830   Which one of your friends would you choose to run a three-legged race with?

831   Have you ever unintentionally said something out loud? What was it?

832   What's the best "going to the bathroom" expression you've heard used?

833   You're sitting next to a crying baby on a plane and there's four hours left to go. What do you do?

834 Do you believe that what goes around comes around?

835 What's your best team-training or buddy-bonding workshop story?

836 If you were a tree, how tall would you want to be?

837 Our galaxy is the Milky Way. What name would you give to a newly discovered galaxy?

838 If you could have one professional home improvement made in your home, what would it be?

839 Have you ever been on a pilgrimage? Would you like to, and where would you go?

840 Will science eventually allow humans to live forever?

841 Can you beatbox? If not, what's your best effort?

842 What three things do you associate with Scotland?

843 Should high-profile sports players quit social media to escape racial abuse?

844 If your skin had to change to a bright color, what color would you like it to be?

845 What's the most miraculous escape story you've ever heard?

846 When did you last visit a public library and did you take out a book?

847 Is it ever okay to steal? Under what circumstances?

848 If Jurassic Park was a real place with actual dinosaurs, would you visit it?

849 What's the meanest (not deadly) act of revenge you've ever heard of?

850 Have you ever felt like you're being watched? When?

851 If you had to get your own "magnificent seven" together, who would be in your posse?

852 What's the craziest car insurance claim story you've heard?

853 Will online shopping see the end of brick-and-mortar shops?

854 Do you share a birthday with anyone famous?

855   What actor who tried a singing career made the biggest mistake?

856   Is it fair to expel students from school?

857   What's the preferred system you use to keep track of appointments and important events?

858   When was the last time you had to swallow your pride?

859   What's the scariest experience you've had or witnessed?

860   Have you ever put something away in a safe place and then forgotten where you put it?

861   What's the most creative and heroic way you can imagine dying?

862   If laughter is the best medicine, what's second best?

863   What's your favorite milkshake flavor?

864   Would you ever consider participating in a paid clinical trial? Why? If so, what would be your minimum compensation amount?

865   What's the craziest autocorrected message you've sent?

866   Which body part would you miss the least if it dropped off?

867   Do you have or have you ever had a lucky charm? What is/was it?

868   What was the last thing you bought that served no real purpose, but you bought just because you liked it?

869   Have you ever been pooped on by a bird or any other animal?

870   What are your top three most frequently used websites for online shopping?

871   Which one of your friends would you not trust as your house sitter or pet sitter, and why?

872   What's the most hurtful thing someone has ever said to you?

873   You combine your three favorite candy bars into a new product. What will you call it?

874   What do you absolutely refuse to believe?

875 Did you like any of the books you had to read for school?

876 What person alive today is least likely to ever become a US President?

877 Have you ever felt misunderstood? When and why?

878 What's your best story of someone swallowing something they shouldn't have?

879 If *Little Red Riding Hood* didn't have a red cloak, what color would it be?

880 What's the classiest garden ornament you've ever seen?

881 Do you have recipe books in your kitchen? If so, which one do you use most often?

882 You've created a cologne. What's its name?

883 What's the most spontaneous thing you've ever done?

884 The skin on your elbow is called the *wenus*. What name would you give the skin on your nose?

885 What makes us human?

886 If you could have one question about your future answered, what would you ask?

887 Have you ever been properly muddy? When was the last time?

888 What's the weirdest top five list you've come across?

889 If you had to go on a raw food diet, what meals would you miss most?

890 Where in the world would you like to be with your friends to see in the next New Year?

891 What's the cleverest restaurant name you've ever seen?

892 Are humans the most advanced species in the universe?

893 Is it ever wrong to do the right thing?

894 On a scale of one to ten, what's the greatest pain you've experienced, and why?

895   What's the most useless invention?

896   When was the last time you had to pull something out of the bag to save the day?

897   If your surname had to be a food, what name would you like?

898   What three things do you consider unforgivable?

899   Have you ever trimmed someone else's toenails? Would you?

900   What's the snobbiest thing you've heard someone say?

901   If you had to have a dental implant in a color other than white, what would you choose?

902   What do you buy less of than most people you know?

903   Will any of the happenings of this week be things you'll remember this time next year?

904   What's your best staycation story?

905   Has anyone ever guessed your age to be way under or over your actual age?

906   What's the most generous tip you've given for good service?

907   Which one of your online usernames would make a great name for a band?

908   What's the most fun science experiment you've ever done at home?

909   People sometimes get a second chance, but would you give someone a third chance?

910   What's your best "tumbleweed moment" story?

911   If you were a vacation destination, which one would you be, and why?

912   What celebrity home do you think shows the worst taste in décor?

913   If you could have VIP access to any event, which one would you choose?

914   What's the tallest building you've been to the top of?

915   Who do you know who is living life to the full?

916   What's the most interesting meal you could make with potatoes as the main ingredient?

917   Do you believe in ghosts and have you ever seen one?

918   What's the funniest shower curtain design you've ever seen?

919   Is it okay for museums, theaters, and art galleries to accept money from fossil-fuel companies?

920   Have you ever flown first class? What airline would you choose if you could?

921   What's the oddest thing you've seen advertised for sale?

922   You've created a brand-new app. What is it?

923   What's the most disturbing true crime story you've heard?

924   How many days of plates have you stacked up before doing the washing up?

925   What do you consider to be the height of bad manners?

926   Were you bullied at school, and do you remember the bully's name?

927   What's the most uncomfortable or awkward thing you've ever had to do out of politeness?

928   Is it possible to be happy if you've never experienced sadness?

929   What would your rapper name be?

930   When do you find you lack discipline?

931   What's the most shocking experiment you've heard of that would never be allowed today?

932   Have you ever been seasick? If so, when?

933   What's the most random item you've put in your shopping cart in a grocery store?

934   Do you hit the recommended 150 minutes of exercise per week target?

935   What's the most mind-blowing illusion you've seen performed by a magician?

936   If you were a wildlife camera operator, what would you hope to capture on film?

937   What's the spookiest sound you've ever heard?

938   Have you ever gone swimming in a river? Where and when?

939   What's the most inappropriate question someone has ever asked you?

940   When was the last time you had to do a double take? Why?

941   What's the most fascinating fact you know about the human body?

942   Did you wear hand-me-down clothes as a child, and would (or do) you wear secondhand clothes now?

943   What's the most bizarre name you've seen for a color of paint?

944   Who's the most sophisticated person you know?

945   What's the oddest compliment someone has paid you?

946   Have you ever discovered you've been calling someone by the wrong name for months?

947   What's the longest you've gone without a bath or a shower?

948   Which celebrities have the best style?

949   What's the most extreme thing you've ever done?

950   Do you still listen to the music you listened to ten years ago?

951   Would you know what to do to help someone bleeding badly after an accident? Have you ever done it?

952   What personality quirk do you have that you wish you didn't?

953   If you could hibernate for the winter, what would you eat first when you woke up?

954   What was the last thing you built from a flat pack or kit?

955   Should horror films no longer be made? Why?

956   What do you currently pay for that should be free for everyone?

957 Have you ever used a traditional map instead of a GPS? When was the last time?

958 Which one of your relatives are you glad your parents didn't name you after?

959 What's the grossest ancient healing belief you've heard of?

960 You don't have enough plates for all your guests. What do you serve food on instead?

961 What's your best school-science-experiment-gone-wrong story?

962 If you had to have an extra limb, what would you want it to be?

963 What actual names would be funny for Daddy Bear, Mummy Bear, and Baby Bear in the story of Goldilocks?

964 Is it possible to have too much choice? When?

965 What three things do you need before it feels like the weekend?

966 Do you feel your age on the inside?

967 What's the worst case of hoarding you've heard of?

968 If meat-free foods had meat-free names, what would be a good name for vegetarian bacon?

969 What was the last thing you changed the batteries in?

970 Have you ever purchased anything from an infomercial? If so, what was it?

971 What's the funniest brand name you've ever seen?

972 Is there a board game you now play online instead of on a board?

973 What makes you cry?

974 You've been tasked with rebranding "Toot Sweets" from *Chitty Chitty Bang Bang*. What name will you go with?

975 What's the biggest unexpected repair bill you've had to pay?

976 When was the last time you had to cover your eyes when watching TV, and why?

977　What do you do differently at home when you have guests?

978　Do you say "shoot" after saying "rock, paper, scissors"?

979　What's the most lost you've ever been, and where were you?

980　If you could host a party in an unusual location, where would it be?

981　What's your best school field day story?

982　Have you ever been skinny dipping? When was the last time?

983　What has been the best "message" you've ever found in a fortune cookie?

984　Who's the most daring real-life hero you know?

985　Which one of your friends has the weirdest laugh? How would you describe it?

986　What music have you listened to most today?

987　A Labrador crossed with a poodle is a labradoodle. What other breeds would you cross to make a great name?

988　What's the best riddle you know?

989　If you had to have stitches that would leave a visible scar, where would you prefer it to be?

990　What movie have you seen with a totally ridiculous plot, but you watched it anyway?

991　Pickleball is a mix of badminton, tennis, and table tennis. What other three sports could combine into a new game?

992　What's been the biggest waste of time in your life?

993　Have you ever used the Forrest Gump line "Life is like a box of chocolates" in real life?

994　What made-up word describes the sound of cheese melting?

995　There are 118 known elements. What would you call the 119th if you discovered it?

996　What would you like to be able to make disappear with just a dab of magic cream?

997 What's something exciting that's happened to you this year?

998 What food outlet would you most like to be receive free food for life from?

999 Where have you gone that felt like you were "boldly going where no man had been before"?

1000 What would be the worst food to use as a sandwich filling?

1001 Is it ever okay to take the law into your own hands?

1002 What happens when an unstoppable force hits an immovable object?

1003 Would you like snakes more if they had fur?

1004 What would be an unlikely line to hear in a *Star Wars* movie?

1005 How many cities can you name beginning with B?

1006 What do you do if a cashier gives you more change than you're due?

1007 If you had to hide 101 dalmatians in your home, where would you put them?

1008 What would be a funny alternative name for Harry Potter?

1009 Have you ever regifted something? What was it?

1010 What will your hobbies be when you retire?

1011 Is someone who hates haters a hater themselves?

1012 What movie explosion is the most awesome?

1013 Who do you know who thinks they are smarter than they actually are?

1014 What was the last gift you bought for someone's birthday?

1015 When have you had too many options?

1016 What image could you use to convey your mood right now?

1017 At what point in your life was your hair at its longest?

1018 What telltale signs appear in your behavior when you're feeling stressed?

1019   You receive a call from an unknown number, do you answer it?

1020   What do you do if the person opposite you at a dinner party is lip-smacking?

1021   If you had to hide a life-size cardboard cutout of The Rock in your home, where would you put it?

1022   What sounds set your teeth on edge?

1023   When was the last time you had hiccups and how did you cure them?

1024   What playing piece do you always want to be in a game of Monopoly?

1025   Have you ever walked a mile in someone else's shoes?

1026   What was the last thing you changed your mind about at the last minute?

1027   You've been tasked with marketing the unhealthiest food you know as a healthy option. How do you do it?

1028   What nursery rhyme can you remember all the words to?

1029   Do you hold grudges, and are you holding any now?

1030   What's your best public changing room or locker room story?

1031   If you could hypnotize a family member, what would you get them to do?

1032   What pet name or term of endearment do you hate being called?

1033   Have you ever been talked into doing something you didn't want to do? What was it?

1034   What three things should never be joked about?

1035   Is there a canned fruit you like better than the fresh variety?

1036   What guitar riff is the greatest ever?

1037   How many single-use items do you use in an average week?

1038   What's the best "dad joke" you know?

1039   Which celebrity chef cooks the type of meals that represent food hell for you?

1040   What new skill could be learned and mastered within one month?

1041   If Middle Earth was real, where do you think it would be?

1042   What do you do if someone you meet at a social event is talking bull but everyone else is sucked in?

1043   Guinea pigs aren't pigs or from Guinea, so what should they be called?

1044   What food would make the top of your comfort food list?

1045   Have you ever walked barefoot outdoors? When and where was the last time?

1046   What's the most expensive meal you've ever eaten and where?

1047   Who's the most artsy-fartsy person you know?

1048   What makes you paranoid?

1049   How many slices of toast could you eat in one sitting? Have you done it?

1050   What facial hair style is your favorite?

1051   Did you catch chickenpox as a kid? If so, how did your parents stop you from scratching?

1052   What pet did you want most when you were a child but could never have?

1053   If money no longer existed, what would you like to be paid with?

1054   What's the last thing you felt you knew for sure?

1055   Have you ever referred to anyone as Mr. or Ms. Fancy-Pants? What were they wearing?

1056   What's the most disgusting sound you've ever heard?

1057   Which one of your friends do you wish had a mute button?

1058   If you could instantly be a master of a martial art, which one would you choose?

1059   What's your best people-watching-at-the-airport story?

1060   You find a spider on your wall at home. What do you do?

1061 What food that you eat have you never seen in its natural, unprocessed state?

1062 How many clocks do you have in your home and do they all keep the correct time?

1063 What souvenir would you most like to bring back from another country?

1064 If you had to match your personality to a breed of dog, which breed would you be?

1065 What added scent would make an unusual bar of soap?

1066 What's the weirdest thing you've seen used to tie up someone's hair?

1067 Is there a conspiracy theory you believe in?

1068 What's the best age to have children?

1069 Would you say you're an artistic person? Why?

1070 What's the most creative use you can come up with for an empty ice cream carton?

1071 Prince William and Kate are coming to your home for tea. What will you offer them to eat?

1072 What global issue will technology solve within the next five years?

1073 Do you keep a journal, and if so, how often do you write in it?

1074 What's the funniest family name you've ever come across?

1075 When was the last time you had butterflies in your stomach?

1076 What have you done recently that made you feel you were turning into your mom or dad?

1077 Should a person be innocent until proven guilty or guilty until proven innocent?

1078 What's the best shadow puppet you can make with your hands?

1079 Who's the most outrageous performer you've seen live on stage?

1080 What's your favorite food to barbecue or grill?

1081 If you had to make clothes out of your curtains, what room would you take them from?

1082 What was the last thing you cooked from scratch?

1083 You've been offered $100,000 to do a ski jump. Would you do it?

1084 What's the best basketball trick shot you've ever seen played?

1085 Which one of your friends can do the best evil laugh?

1086 What's the best email address you've ever seen?

1087 Have you ever gone singing and dancing in the rain?

1088 What land animal would be most awesome if it could swim underwater?

1089 What would your WWE (World Wrestling Entertainment) name be?

1090 If you were an assassin, who would be at the top of your hit list?

1091 Do you think robots will replace teachers in schools?

1092 What three things do you value most in a friend?

1093 What do you do if you accidentally swallow a fly?

1094 Have you ever walked out of a movie theater before the end of the movie? Why?

1095 What would you have done to get yourself onto a lifeboat if you'd been on the *Titanic*?

1096 Is there a food from another country that's impossible to get in your country?

1097 What motto would you say you live by?

1098 Where have you been that felt like the middle of nowhere?

1099 Is all fair in love and war? Why or why not?

1100 What's your best pancake tossing story?

1101 How many songs can you think of that have numbers in the title or lyrics?

1102 What's the most creative thing you've written with when you couldn't find a pen?

1103 Which movie would you like to see retold from a different point of view?

1104 What's the most amazing thing you've seen a trained animal do?

1105 If you had to make one part of your body bigger, what would it be?

1106 What would happen if a vampire bit a zombie?

1107 Have you ever flown a kite? If so, when was the last time?

1108 What's the best car windshield sunshade you've seen?

1109 Do you believe in love at first sight? Has it happened to you?

1110 What's the lowest you'll let your phone battery go before you charge it?

1111 When in your life has there been no going back?

1112 What should we use to measure success instead of fame and fortune?

1113 If you could invent a time-saving device, what would it be for?

1114 You're driving on the road and the car behind is intentionally tailgating you. What do you do?

1115 Would you risk losing a $500,000 prize if you were 75 percent sure you could win $1,000,000?

1116 What name is least likely to ever be given to a royal baby?

1117 There are five of you and only one slice of pizza left. What do you do?

1118 What petty annoyance has impacted your day today?

1119 Have you ever received a Valentine's card from a mystery admirer who remained a mystery?

1120 What would be a great name for a racing greyhound?

1121 Which celebrity do you wish had never been born?

1122 What world event in your lifetime will be discussed in history classes in a hundred years' time?

1123 Who do you owe most to?

1124 What one rule should never, ever be broken?

1125 If you had to move to a new city, how would you make new friends?

1126 What might the three little pigs have made their houses out of in a parallel universe?

1127 When was the last time you had a snowball fight and who with?

1128 *What would your signature bake be on The Great American Baking Show (Great British Bake Off)?*

1129 Do you own a watch or piece of jewelry that used to belong to a relative?

1130 What's the weirdest thing you've slept on or in?

1131 Have you ever wished on a star and did your wish come true?

1132 What song would you say is your anthem?

1133 An extra month is added to the calendar. What will it be called?

1134 What three things that you have now would you give up to get the one thing you really want?

1135 How many steps do you take in a day? Do you aim for ten thousand?

1136 What team name would be hilariously ridiculous if cheerleaders had to spell it out?

1137 Who would you most like to shadow for the day to learn how they handle life?

1138 What was the last competitive thing you did?

1139 If money were no object, where would you choose to eat tonight?

1140 What makes you sentimental?

1141 Do you know any words that mean something very different in another country?

1142 What's the best comeback you've heard when someone's height has been ridiculed?

1143   Which one of your friends best fits the description of "loud and proud"?

1144   If you were an author, what pen name would you use?

1145   What will cause the extinction of humanity?

1146   You've been given the lead role in a biopic. Who are you portraying?

1147   What's your best hot tub story?

1148   If New York City cabs weren't yellow, what color should they be?

1149   What word is fun to say?

1150   Have you ever forgotten a family member's birthday?

1151   What would be a cool rival company name for Amazon?

1152   Does being an only child mean you miss out on life?

1153   What word could you invent to describe one of your persistent habits?

1154   If you could live in a video game world for a day, which would you choose?

1155   What games did you play in your childhood that kids today have never heard of?

1156   Have you ever wished you could be in two places at once? When, and where did you want to be?

1157   What do you do if you can't sleep?

1158   You've been granted access for a private tour of any company or facility in the world. What do you choose and why?

1159   Queen Victoria did it. Have you ever dunked a biscuit in a cup of tea?

1160   What was the last DIY project you did?

1161   How did you celebrate your last birthday?

1162   What's the best monument or landmark you've seen lit up at night?

1163   When was the last time you had a nosebleed? Where were you?

1164 What would be an appropriate punishment for people who eat food from your plate?

1165 If no water was available, what would be your next choice to quench your thirst?

1166 What was the last thing you couldn't help bragging about?

1167 You get asked to design a new Lego set. What would it be?

1168 What superpower would you least like to have, and why?

1169 Where do you think the lost city of Atlantis will be found?

1170 What would paradise look like for you?

1171 Can you come up with a sportswear brand tagline that beats "Just do it!"?

1172 What five things would you put in a time capsule to be dug up in twenty-five years?

1173 If you had to power your home by pedaling a bike, what would you do differently?

1174 What would you do if you were being charged at by an angry elephant?

1175 Have you ever been the last to know something? What was it?

1176 What's the loudest thing you've ever heard?

1177 You've been summoned to jury duty and it's for a high-profile case. Do you serve or try and get excused?

1178 What's the last purchase or donation you made to a thrift store?

1179 Which one of your friends best fits the description of an "ideas machine"?

1180 It's mid-afternoon and you want a snack. What's your preferred snack food?

1181 How many things do you carry in your pockets, and what are they?

1182 What additional feature will all future cars have?

1183 Do you feel strongly enough about something to go on a protest march? What is it?

1184   What, if anything, makes you feel most patriotic?

1185   Have you ever found it funny when you've hit your funny bone?

1186   What's the best food that comes on a stick?

1187   Would you thumb a ride if your car had broken down and you had no phone?

1188   What's the longest time you've been kept on hold on the phone?

1189   How many things do you leave plugged in twenty-four hours a day?

1190   What do you do if you see someone walk out of a public toilet with paper stuck on their shoe?

1191   Should jousting be an Olympic sport?

1192   What's your best home-remedy-gone-wrong story?

1193   Is there a food or drink item that your hometown is famed for?

1194   What's something that's now lost and will never be found?

1195   When it's your ninetieth birthday, which family members will you have around you to celebrate?

1196   Who would you most like to have a signed photo of?

1197   What hurricane or storm name should be added to the list?

1198   If you had to rename Smurfs, what name would you go for?

1199   What song lyrics have you misheard?

1200   Did you leave a snack for Santa and his reindeer when you were little? What was it?

1201   What's the best prank pulled by identical twins that you've heard of?

1202   If you were an Olympic swimmer, what stroke would be your strongest?

1203   What three things would you change about your job if you could?

1204   When was the last time you gave someone flowers?

1205 What might Yankee Doodle have stuck in his cap in a parallel universe?

1206 Have you ever gone through a day believing that the events of the previous night's dream happened for real?

1207 What phrase would you like to add to candy hearts?

1208 You've been buried alive in an avalanche. What do you do?

1209 Which one of the seven dwarfs would you be?

1210 What's the best personalized license plate you've seen?

1211 Do you know anyone guilty of using computerese or tech talk unnecessarily?

1212 What one experience would you like to experience again for the first time?

1213 Has anyone ever told you something you wish they hadn't? What was it?

1214 What do you do if you've forgotten someone's name and you have to introduce them to someone else?

1215 Have you heard of water tasters or odor prospectors? What's the weirdest real job you've heard of?

1216 What was the last thing you deleted by accident?

1217 If you had to replace your right foot with the foot of an animal, what animal would you choose?

1218 What once-in-a-lifetime experience would you like to be able to repeat?

1219 Who do you think should be crowned the king of pop?

1220 What new emoji would you like to create, and when would you use it?

1221 There are no guarantees in life, but if there were, what one thing would you like to be guaranteed?

1222 What might Hogwarts be a school of in a parallel universe?

1223 Do you believe in fate? Why?

1224 What do you do to escape from someone who won't stop talking?

1225   If you could make a warning sound like a rattlesnake, which part of your body would make it, and what sound would it make?

1226   What's your best haircut horror story?

1227   A breakdancing magician? What skill combo would be highly entertaining?

1228   What movie have you watched the most and how many times have you watched it?

1229   Have you ever cried at a TV commercial?

1230   What was the last thing you did that made you sweat?

1231   If music didn't exist, how different would your life be?

1232   What message would you like to put on the inside of a Dove Chocolate Promise wrapper?

1233   Ring camera? What everyday item could you cunningly disguise to create a James Bond weapon?

1234   What hand signal or gesture is the most universally known and means the same everywhere?

1235   Would you stroke a cockroach?

1236   What was the last event or appointment you canceled?

1237   Is there a seat in your house that's reserved for only one person?

1238   What have you been reminded of lately that you would really rather forget?

1239   Which celebrity would you most like to be stuck in an elevator with?

1240   What's the longest bridge you've gone across and where was it?

1241   Should it be mandatory for people earning a salary above $200,000 to contribute to charity? Why?

1242   What's the longest you've gone without speaking to someone close to you?

1243   If you had to run from danger, how far would you get before collapsing?

1244   What Guinness World Record would you most like to hold?

1245   Is happiness a choice?

1246   When was the last time you gave or received a handmade gift? What was it?

1247   What might *The Lion, the Witch and the Wardrobe* be called in a parallel universe?

1248   How many things do you need a physical key for, and which key would be the toughest to replace?

1249   What's the weirdest thing you've seen strapped on the roof of a car?

1250   How many children are too many children in one family?

1251   What flavor of jelly bean should be introduced?

1252   If music played every time you sneezed, what music would you like it to be?

1253   What makes you smile every time you see it?

1254   Do you agree that live music always sounds better at an outdoor venue?

1255   What do you do to wake yourself up in the morning?

1256   Have you ever gone to the cinema on your own? Would you?

1257   You're gifted one piece of jewelry with an unlimited budget; what item do you choose?

1258   Who would you like to challenge to a water pistol duel?

1259   What one file on your computer is the most important one?

1260   Curiosity killed the cat. What's the worst trouble curiosity got you into?

1261   What has been your favorite Google doodle?

1262   If you were arrested by the police, what would it be for?

1263   You've been asked to write an original verse for a greetings card. What would you write?

1264   What slang word from a generation ago should make a comeback?

1265   If you could make a wish that would come true for someone else, what would it be?

1266 What three things would you never buy without first reading reviews?

1267 What make was your first cell phone?

1268 You get the chance to visit the NASA International Space Station, but you need to stay for six months. Would you go?

1269 When was the last time you stood up for someone?

1270 If Nike had to rebrand, what would a good name be?

1271 What's your best gym or exercise class story?

1272 Have you ever found out something you weren't supposed to know by accident? What was it?

1273 Which device do you primarily use to take photos?

1274 Who would miss you most if you vanished right now?

1275 What movie always makes you laugh, no matter how many times you see it?

1276 If you had to spend $1,000 within the next hour, what would you buy?

1277 What style of jeans do you wear most, and why?

1278 Where and under what circumstances would you least like to audibly break wind?

1279 If you could make it against the law to do something for one day, what would it be?

1280 What was the last thing you did that gave you an adrenaline rush?

1281 Had Harry Houdini not died, what would his next escape have been?

1282 What never ends well?

1283 When people mispronounce your name, what do they call you?

1284 What was the last hashtag you created?

1285 You've been asked to name three baby penguins at the zoo. What names will you give them?

1286   If not "who's the daddy?" what do you say when you win something?

1287   What age do you think people should retire at?

1288   Is there a food you only eat in winter, never summer?

1289   What would be a fabulous new aroma for a scented candle?

1290   If your feet increased a size every time you thought about food today, what size shoe would you be wearing now?

1291   When was the last time you found yourself speechless and why?

1292   What physical attribute is most striking in a beautiful person?

1293   Have you ever won an argument and then discovered you were wrong? What was the argument about?

1294   What would be an appropriate punishment for people who hog the middle lane on freeways?

1295   Do you know anyone who can wiggle their ears?

1296   What non-toxic thing will you absolutely not touch with your bare hands?

1297   Have you ever found something you'd forgotten about in a coat pocket? What was it?

1298   What's the last thing you recommended to someone?

1299   Which one of the Mr. Men or Little Miss characters is most like you?

1300   If you had to stick to the same meal plan every week, what would you eat every Wednesday?

1301   What would make a fun alternative to standard chess pieces?

1302   Would you walk over hot coals if given the opportunity?

1303   What should there be a new encyclopedia of?

1304   How many times did you get detention in school? For what reasons?

1305   What song do you think is the best to help you keep up the rhythm when doing CPR?

1306 Should loot boxes in video games be banned for children?

1307 What's your best fancy restaurant story?

1308 Is there a food you'll never, ever try?

1309 What stories have you heard of things caught on "nanny cams"?

1310 Allowing for inflation, what do you think it would it cost to rebuild the Six Million Dollar Man today?

1311 What thought enters your mind when you see a single shoe lying on the side of the road?

1312 If you were asked to write your life story for publication, would you hire a ghostwriter?

1313 As you're walking, you notice a lady sitting on a bench crying. What do you do?

1314 What would you do if you saw someone shoplift a can of beans?

1315 Has anyone ever said you're their hero? What had you done?

1316 What do you do when people are talking loudly in a movie theater?

1317 Robert Burns wrote a poem to his haggis. Which food would you write a poem to?

1318 What's the last thing you touched that was too hot to handle?

1319 Which of your spray-on products has the best smell?

1320 What will be the next thing to be banned?

1321 You've been asked to radically redesign $10 bills. What will your design be?

1322 Which character from the *Jungle Book* would you most like to hang out with?

1323 Who has the best GPS voice?

1324 What was your lowest performing subject at school? Did you ever fail a subject?

1325 How many books do you read on average in a year?

1326 What would be a good mask for a bank robber to wear today?

1327 You've been asked to invent a new flavor of ice cream; what would it be?

1328 What's never as good the second time around as it is the first time around?

1329 When was the last time you felt totally confused? Why?

1330 What makes a perfectly cooked steak?

1331 If not a billy goat and a nanny goat, what other names would be fun for male and female goats?

1332 What would be the worst thing to say at a wedding?

1333 There are tea bags and coffee bags; what else should come in bags?

1334 What's the best good news story you've heard recently?

1335 If you could make one minor upgrade to the human body, what would it be?

1336 What's the weirdest thing you've seen turned into a musical instrument?

1337 Is there a holiday that's outdated and could use a revamp?

1338 What would you do if you knew you couldn't fail?

1339 You've been asked to name a new beauty salon and spa. What will you name it?

1340 What's been your worst hair or beauty disaster?

1341 Who were you with when you re-enacted the "Bohemian Rhapsody" scene from *Wayne's World?*

1342 What's the best home remedy for constipation you've heard of?

1343 Do you believe that a leopard never changes its spots?

1344 What was the last thing you did that made you want to kick yourself?

1345 How different would your life be if cell phones had never been invented?

1346 What's your best dinosaur fact?

1347 Have you ever been sunburned?

1348   What do you do when someone invades your personal space?

1349   If you had to swap fingers with one of your friends, who would you choose to swap with?

1350   What's the coolest magic trick you've ever seen?

1351   Would your friends describe you as the man/woman for an emergency?

1352   Could you get through your day if you could only use one arm?

1353   What's the best anti-aging tip you ever heard, and have you tried it?

1354   Is there a long-standing tradition in your family? What is it?

1355   What's the coolest thing you've seen made of recycled materials?

1356   Have you ever had a cold shower, and was it by choice?

1357   What's the first sign of spring each year?

1358   If you were born on February 29th, on what date would you celebrate your birthday in non-leap years?

1359   Do professional sports players get paid too much? Which ones in particular?

1360   What's the highest score you've ever achieved on a test?

1361   If not a giant beanstalk, what would your magic beans grow into?

1362   What's the longest amount of time you've spent indoors without going outside at all?

1363   You get to add one word to the book of life. Which word will it be?

1364   What do you do when you're approached by beggars on the street?

1365   Is there a name for a combined yawn and burp?

1366   What's the longest you've gone without sleep, and why?

1367   How many bones in your body do you know the medical terms for?

1368   What's the most beautiful thing you see every day?

1369 When was the last time you felt the wind in your hair?

1370 What's the most outrageous color of pants you've ever worn (not on a golf course!)?

1371 If you could make origami towels, what shape would you make?

1372 What's the most interesting thing you've learned through watching a documentary?

1373 When you're searching for ideas, where do you go to find them?

1374 What's the most romantic thing someone has ever done for you?

1375 You've been asked to create a themed room in a hotel. What theme would you choose?

1376 When something good happens to you, who is the first person you want to tell about it?

1377 What's the one thing you know you're really good at?

1378 Have you ever given anything a zero rating in a feedback questionnaire? What was it?

1379 What pizza topping should never have been invented?

1380 Who was your least favorite teacher at school, and why?

1381 What's the riskiest thing you've ever done?

1382 How many times do you chew your food before swallowing?

1383 What's the most disgusting food combination your friends eat?

1384 As a child, what songs did you sing or games did you play in the car on long journeys?

1385 Have you ever had a great idea that turned out to be a bad idea?

1386 What do you find a breeze that many others find a challenge?

1387 What's your best bounce-house story?

1388 Do you believe in UFOs, and have you seen one?

1389 What's the longest time you've been stuck in a traffic jam? Where were you going?

1390 If not a ponytail, what animal part would be a good way to describe your hair?

1391 What three words would you use to describe the feeling of being in love?

1392 Have you ever been the center of attention when you didn't want to be? When?

1393 What's the cutest thing you've ever seen?

1394 Is there a reason for everything?

1395 What additional rule would make marathon running a more interesting spectator sport?

1396 You are a notorious cat burglar. What's been your most daring theft?

1397 What was the last thing you did that you don't like when other people do it?

1398 How many times do you look at your phone on an average day?

1399 Which of your battery-operated gadgets needs the most batteries?

1400 What meal could you make using only the items in your fridge right now?

1401 Shorts combined with a skirt are *skorts.* What other clothing combo could you create and what would you call it?

1402 What makes you sure that you're not living in a computer simulation?

1403 Can thought influence reality? How?

1404 What's one thing you wouldn't do for health reasons?

1405 Have you ever had a gut feeling that something bad was going to happen and then it did?

1406 What do you find most distracting when you're trying to concentrate?

1407 Is there a place where you're no longer welcome? Where and why?

1408 What would you like to teach a parrot to say?

1409 Does every cloud have a silver lining?

1410   What's the most ridiculous thing you've ever accidentally poked yourself in the eye with?

1411   When was the last time you felt sand between your toes?

1412   If you could name a new shape, what shape would it be and what would you call it?

1413   Which one of your friends or family members has the noisiest way of blowing their nose?

1414   Have you heard of the ice bucket challenge? What new fundraiser would you devise to raise money for charity?

1415   What would need to happen today for you to be in a better mood than you are now?

1416   If you were compiling a book of family favorite recipes, what would go in the dessert section?

1417   What's the most introverted thing you've ever done to avoid other people?

1418   Should marriage be a contract that can be renewed or canceled on an annual basis?

1419   Which character from the *Thomas the Tank Engine* stories are you most like?

1420   Who has the coolest tattoos and what's cool about them?

1421   What's the most amazing story an old person has told you?

1422   Have you ever worn socks in bed?

1423   What would be the funniest shape to trim a garden hedge into?

1424   If you had to take part in a field day wheelbarrow race, which part of the wheelbarrow would you be?

1425   What's the weirdest thing you've heard of a fan asking their idol to sign?

1426   You've been asked to create a new family board game; what three ideas will you trial?

1427   What were you researching when you last fell into a Wikipedia rabbit hole?

1428   Who was your first kiss with and when was it?

1429 Which of your bad habits would you find hardest to break?

1430 What sport did you enjoy playing most at school?

1431 How many times have you looked in a mirror today?

1432 If you could never have hot food again, what meal would you miss most?

1433 What's the highest above sea level you've ever been and where were you?

1434 When you're getting dressed, do you always put items on in the same order?

1435 What one question will always remain unanswerable?

1436 Hamburgers don't contain ham. What other foods have names that don't seem to relate to what they are?

1437 Do you identify more with Coke or Pepsi and why?

1438 What's your best babysitting or babysitter story?

1439 Did you ever push something up your nose or in your ear as a child? What was it?

1440 What do you have that money can't buy?

1441 There can only be one TV channel. Which one should it be?

1442 What plain-colored animal would look coolest with stripes?

1443 Have you ever had a haircut to look like a celebrity?

1444 Which movie is crying out for a sequel?

1445 What's the coolest victory dance you've seen anyone do?

1446 Are there any playground games you played as a kid that have now been banned?

1447 What's the best prize you've ever won in a competition?

1448 Which of the seven deadly sins are you most guilty of?

1449 You need to convince someone that the world is flat. What's your strongest proof or evidence?

1450 What three words would you use to describe your personal style?

1451 If you were cremated, where would you want your ashes scattered?

1452 What's the best piece of advice anyone ever gave you?

1453 Which of the outfits you own would be the most ridiculous to wear on an outdoor activity day?

1454 Who was the popular kid in your school and why were they so popular?

1455 What's been the messiest thing you've accidentally dropped?

1456 How many times would you fail your driving test before giving up?

1457 What famous person would you least like to be paired with as a ballroom dance partner?

1458 When things go bump in the night, what do you think those things are?

1459 If not a fat lady singing, what else would let you know it's all over?

1460 What was the last thing you did that you instantly regretted doing?

1461 Is there a social media influencer that you admire, and why?

1462 What's the best thing to have on toast?

1463 You go to your locker after a swim and discover your shoes have vanished; what do you do?

1464 What's the weirdest thing you've heard of people putting on a hot dog?

1465 Have you ever wound anything up by hand or with a key? What was it?

1466 What's the rarest thing in the world?

1467 When was the last time you felt out of your comfort zone and what were you doing?

1468 What forgotten item would you least like to find in a coat pocket?

1469 How many unfinished projects do you have right now?

1470 What might be different about Snow White and the Seven Dwarfs in a parallel universe?

1471   Has anything ever made you appear guilty, even though you were innocent? What was it?

1472   What are the most northerly and southerly points you've visited on a world map?

1473   For what one thing do you think the legal age could be lowered?

1474   What do you have that you would like better if it was a different color?

1475   You've been asked to coin a catchphrase for Greta Thunberg. What will it be?

1476   What land animal would be the most spectacular if it sprouted wings and could fly?

1477   If you could never leave your home again, what would you miss most?

1478   What musical instrument creates the saddest sound?

1479   What's your best "tried to be really quiet but ended up being really noisy" story?

1480   How many verses of your national anthem can you sing by heart?

1481   What would you do to get the attention of a room full of noisy children?

1482   Do you (or would you) discipline your children in the same way your parents disciplined you?

1483   What have you done recently that you hope no one saw you doing?

1484   If not a pail of water, what else might Jack and Jill have gone up the hill for?

1485   What facial feature do you have that you'd never want to change?

1486   How different would your life be if you didn't have internet access?

1487   What food would you never want to eat on a first date?

1488   When was the last time you felt on top of the world and why?

1489   What would be the most ridiculous substitute for the ponies in the Pony Express?

1490   If you could never watch TV again, what show would you miss most?

1491 What new character would make a good addition to the suspects in Clue (Cluedo)?

1492 Have you ever had a magazine subscription? Which one?

1493 What album do you love every single track on?

1494 Which slang word do you use most?

1495 Can you usually name a song just by hearing the intro?

1496 What's your best "there ain't no such thing as a free lunch" story?

1497 If not a tortoise and a hare, what other two animals would make mismatched race competitors?

1498 What thing that money can't buy would you most like to have?

1499 If you were given one million dollars to help others, what would you do with it?

1500 Which chocolate do you always choose from the box if you get first pick?

1501 If you had to walk backward for a day, what bit of your day would be most awkward?

1502 What would be a hilarious topic for prolific songwriter Ed Sheeran to write a song about?

1503 When you were ten, what age did you think was really old?

1504 Have you ever rescued an animal? What was it?

1505 What time of day do you like best?

1506 You need to declutter your living space. Which three things could you part with right now?

1507 What song or tune has been stuck in your head recently?

1508 Do you agree that there's always someone worse off than yourself?

1509 What famous quote would make the best advertising slogan for a shoe company?

1510 Have you ever been the only person in the room not to get the joke? What was the joke?

1511   What was the last thing you did to treat yourself?

1512   How many times do you boil a kettle on an average day?

1513   What non-lethal and non-physically violent method of torture would be most effective?

1514   Is there a song you used to really like until you discovered what the message in the lyrics really was?

1515   What famous person (living or dead) would you like to have as a mentor?

1516   Who have you hated for the longest time, and will you ever not hate them?

1517   At what age are you too old to street dance?

1518   What playground game would make a great Olympic sport?

1519   Is there a tall tale your grandparents told you that you were never quite sure whether to believe?

1520   What music do you find most irritating when you're put on hold?

1521   Should mass balloon releases be banned?

1522   What GIF have you shared with others most recently?

1523   Have you heard of Stinking Bishop or Ticklemore cheeses? What would be a great new cheese name?

1524   What do you have today that you didn't have this time last year?

1525   When was the first time you ate with chopsticks?

1526   What myth would you most like to be able to bust?

1527   Do you know anyone who has let a tiny amount of power go to their head?

1528   What's your best "priceless item found in dumpster" story?

1529   You're writing a pop song. What lyrics do you rhyme with "She had jet-black hair . . ."?

1530   What punishment should people who drop litter be given?

1531   If you could no longer chew, what food would you miss eating most?

1532   Which one of your friends has the worst table manners?

1533   What were the most common names for babies in the year you were born?

1534   Have you ever wondered what would happen if every flushing toilet on Earth was flushed at once?

1535   What store would you most like to have a $500 gift card for?

1536   Who was the last person you went to the cinema with and what movie did you see?

1537   What technology of today will become obsolete first?

1538   There's a cow-tree in the Amazon. What's the weirdest plant you've heard of?

1539   What would be a handy addition to have built in to a wristwatch?

1540   If you were going to be stuck in an elevator for several hours, what food would you want brought to you?

1541   What three things make a person likeable?

1542   You have $100 to improve someone else's life today. What do you do with it?

1543   What skill do you have that would keep you alive in a zombie apocalypse?

1544   Did you ever do the mannequin challenge? What was your pose?

1545   What would be the most shocking thing to discover on Mars?

1546   When was the last time you felt like you'd made a difference?

1547   What non-banned item would be a scary thing to take on a plane?

1548   It's dark and stormy outside. Would you answer an unexpected knock at your door?

1549   What names did you give to your two favorite toys as a child?

1550   Have you ever cried tears of happiness? When was the last time?

1551   What was the last thing you downloaded?

1552 If you had to swap teeth with an animal for the day, what one would you choose?

1553 What would you say you've done to make the world a better place?

1554 Do you fear robots taking over the world? Why?

1555 What's the best purchase you ever made at a dollar store?

1556 Have you ever gone to work (or school) wearing yesterday's underpants?

1557 What job do you think is most underrated and why?

1558 How much money is enough money?

1559 What's the craziest thing you've done when you've been sleep deprived?

1560 Is there a taste you can always detect, even if people try to disguise it?

1561 You need to make a gluten-free vegan lunch. What do you make?

1562 Have you heard of triffids or piranha plants? What name would you give a fictional man-eating plant?

1563 What tiny achievement always feels like a really big achievement to you?

1564 If not as "old as the hills," what else might things be as old as?

1565 What advice would you give your ten-year-old self?

1566 Has anyone ever said you remind them of someone famous? Who was it?

1567 What's the grossest thing you've ever seen in a jar?

1568 When was the last time you felt like screaming at someone and what had they done?

1569 What food should people be banned from eating in confined public spaces?

1570 Do you agree that there's "no such thing as a stupid question"?

1571 What do you love more than cats love boxes?

1572 Have you ever fried an egg on the hood of a car?

3000 UNIQUE QUESTIONS ABOUT ME

80

1573 What's the laziest yet incredibly ingenious thing you've seen someone do?

1574 If not cloud nine, what cloud number would you like to be on, and why?

1575 What alternative medals might be presented in the Olympics in a parallel universe?

1576 Who was the last person you visited in hospital?

1577 What's the most impressive natural sight you've seen?

1578 Is there a type of music that you just can't listen to? What is it?

1579 What's the single most important thing needed to make a relationship work?

1580 Which one of your friends is the moodiest, and what do you do to snap them out of a cranky mood?

1581 What's the solution to endangered animals eating endangered plants?

1582 You're writing a poem. What do you rhyme with "looking at the sun"?

1583 What's your best "neighbors-from-hell" story?

1584 If you could only buy one new item of clothing in a year, what would it be?

1585 What new flavor of potato chip would you like to create?

1586 How many bands can you think of with a number in their name?

1587 What's the weirdest thing you could bury today to confuse future archaeologists?

1588 Have you ever been to a drive-in movie theater?

1589 What has turned out to be much harder than you anticipated?

1590 How much money would you need to win on the lottery before you would give up your job?

1591 What poem or speech would you most like to be able to recite by heart?

1592 Where were you when you last saw a fireworks display?

1593 What's the best thing you've seen on TV that you happened upon by chance?

1594   Who in your family is the biggest tea connoisseur?

1595   What's the most unusual mode of transport you've used?

1596   If you were handed conscription papers in WWI, would you have been a conscientious objector?

1597   What's the most desperate thing you've seen new parents doing to try to get a baby to sleep?

1598   Have you ever given someone an unkind nickname? What was it?

1599   What's the softest thing you've ever touched?

1600   When was the last time someone asked you for help? What did they need help with?

1601   What food are you almost embarrassed to say you like?

1602   How much of a head start would you need on Usain Bolt to get from your kitchen to the bathroom first?

1603   What's the most uncomfortable item you've ever worn in the name of fashion?

1604   Which college degree is least helpful in terms of finding a job?

1605   What's the most ridiculous excuse you've heard for not showing up somewhere that turned out to be true?

1606   If not curved, what shape should bananas be?

1607   What time was bedtime when you were ten?

1608   It's Saturday night and the power will be out for at least two hours. What will you do?

1609   What hairstyle have you had that makes you cringe when you see old photographs?

1610   You need to remove a firmly fixed adhesive bandage from your leg. How do you do it?

1611   What was the last thing you dreaded doing that turned out to be not as bad as you imagined?

1612   Were you afraid to go back in the water after seeing *Jaws*?

1613   What's the best thing about being you?

1614   If you could only have a sixty-second shower once a week, which body parts would you target?

1615   Which one of your friends or family has the cheesiest feet?

1616   When you were little, did you have a funny word for something because you couldn't say the real word? What was it?

1617   What's the most despicable thing you've ever done?

1618   Do you agree that crime never pays? Why?

1619   What's the most amazing photo you've seen taken by a camera drone?

1620   Has anyone ever shown you a prized possession you found slightly creepy? What was it?

1621   What new color of toilet paper should be available?

1622   When was the last time you felt Lady Luck was smiling on you?

1623   What's the most amazing thing you've seen a balloon artist make?

1624   If you had to wear clown shoes for a day, what would you find most difficult?

1625   What tool would be a great addition to a Swiss army knife?

1626   You need to prepare a meal with lentils as the main ingredient. What will you make?

1627   What's your best "knock, knock" joke?

1628   If you were holding a workplace (or school) Olympics, what events would you include?

1629   What's your favorite inspirational quote?

1630   Should organ donation should be mandatory?

1631   What's the furthest in advance you've bought tickets for something?

1632 Is there a TV cartoon that's been ruined by a remake since your childhood?

1633 What's the funniest rumor you've ever heard about yourself?

1634 You have a pet dragon. What have you named it?

1635 What do you need to change about yourself to become the person you want to be?

1636 How difficult would your life become if you tried to stop taking flights?

1637 What new hall of fame would you like to propose and who would be the first person in it?

1638 If not diamonds, what are a girl's best friend?

1639 What's the best put-down you've ever used or heard used?

1640 There's a Gum Wall in Seattle. What else could you stick on a wall to make it famous?

1641 What had you done (or not done) the last time someone got to say "I told you so!"?

1642 Who was the last person you thought about punching in the face (but didn't)?

1643 If you had to wear a hat every day for the rest of your life, what sort of hat would you choose?

1644 What's the biggest thing you ever built with Lego bricks?

1645 You're writing a novel about insects taking over the world. What's its title?

1646 Which one of your friends or family has the funniest way of sneezing?

1647 How many bands can you think of that have a color in their name?

1648 What toy would you like to see added to the characters in *Toy Story*?

1649 If you could change your accent, which one would you choose?

1650 What do you now accept that you always pushed back against in the past?

1651 Could you land a plane in an emergency if air traffic control talked you through it?

1652 What's the best tribute band name you've heard of?

1653 Were you ever given a gold star for your work in school? If not, did you want one?

1654 What food do you wish was poisonous so you wouldn't eat any more of it?

1655 If you could only have one color of T-shirt, what would it be, and why?

1656 What was the last thing you felt the need to have a five-minute rant about?

1657 Have you ever grown anything from a seed? What was it and did it survive?

1658 What's your best "found this in a blocked pipe" story?

1659 Do you know anyone who looks like their pet?

1660 What's the weirdest thing you've ever written an essay on?

1661 You need to remove one social media app from your phone; which one will it be?

1662 What's one ridiculous excuse you've given for not doing something you should have done?

1663 How much time do you spend on the internet on an average day?

1664 What popular trend do you find most annoying, and why?

1665 Everything in moderation is okay, but what shouldn't be done in moderation?

1666 Do you tend to Google your problems?

1667 Have you ever retold a fake news story that you thought was real? What was it?

1668 What do you often see in your home area that visitors will travel miles to see?

1669 Did you have acne as a teenager, and what's your best tip for dealing with it?

1670 Which color of jelly bean tastes best?

1671 If not cotton and linen paper, what would be a fun material to make dollar bills out of?

1672 Have you ever had (or do you have) a collection of something? What?

1673 What do you put salt on?

1674 Who was the last person you spoke to on a landline?

1675 What food do you always put tomato ketchup on?

1676 If you were in a movie, who would you most like to walk off into the sunset with?

1677 You're writing a crime novel. Where will the serial killer hide the bodies?

1678 What always cheers you up when you're having a bad day?

1679 If you had to work in sales, what product would you least like to sell?

1680 When you were little, did you think the moon was made of cheese?

1681 A Milky Way bar in the US is a Mars bar in the UK. What other product name changes do you know of?

1682 When was the last time someone really surprised you, and what did they do?

1683 If you could only have one flavor of potato chip for the rest of your life, what would it be?

1684 What's the best T-shirt slogan you've ever seen?

1685 Were you, or anyone you knew, into the emo scene?

1686 Which nursery rhyme character can you most identify with?

1687 How much time would you save if you could teleport to and from work (or school)?

1688 What trend did you desperately want to follow when you were younger but your parents wouldn't let you?

1689 It's pants in the US and trousers in the UK. What would be a good universal term?

1690 What's your top tip for preventing headphone wires from getting in a knot?

1691 Have you ever had (or thought about having) anything printed on a T-shirt? What was it?

1692   What one person in your life can you always make time for?

1693   If you had your own advice column, what sort of questions would you like to answer?

1694   What's the best type of sausage?

1695   Who was the last person you sent a picture to? What was the picture?

1696   What's your best "class clown" story?

1697   You only have time to grab one possession from your home. What is it?

1698   What do you own (or have owned) with your name engraved on it?

1699   Can you remember your first slumber party? Who came?

1700   What's the biggest crowd you've been in, and where were you?

1701   How often do you change the color scheme or rearrange the furniture in your home?

1702   What's the biggest family dinner or dinner party disaster you've ever had?

1703   Who is the biggest drama queen you know?

1704   What food is more effort to eat than it's worth?

1705   Have you got a name for sneezing and farting at the same time?

1706   What are you saving up for?

1707   What trimmings go best with a roast dinner?

1708   Do you agree that there's an exception to every rule?

1709   What's a suitable punishment for people who drink from the milk carton and then return it to the fridge?

1710   How many bands with four members can you name?

1711   What was the last thing you fixed?

1712   Have you ever had a black eye? When and why?

1713   If you were in *Seinfeld,* which character would you be?

1714   What's your top tip for peeling a pineapple?

1715   You have a boat that needs a name; what will you call it?

1716   If a friend asked for an honest opinion, would you give it—no matter what?

1717   What do you say when you make a toast with a drink?

1718   Have you ever had a Nerf gun battle? When was the last time?

1719   If not gold, what would be the most awesome thing the Midas touch could turn things into?

1720   What tune would you like your washing machine to play to let you know it's done?

1721   Should parents ask for their child's permission before posting photos of them on social media?

1722   What do you spend way too much time on?

1723   There's a scratching sound coming from your garbage can. What do you least want to find in there?

1724   What pose would you like to be in if you were turned to stone?

1725   If you could only have one pair of shoes (or item of footwear), which would you choose?

1726   What one thing are you glad you will never have to do again?

1727   Do you agree that the book is always better than the movie?

1728   What's the weirdest survey you've ever been asked to take part in?

1729   Have you ever completed an online study course? On what topic?

1730   What's the best way to make and serve hot chocolate?

1731   If you had unlimited funds and time, what five countries or places would you visit first?

1732   Which musical instrument do you dislike the most?

1733 You are somehow teleported six feet to the right of where you are now. Would you survive in that location?

1734 What are you superstitious about?

1735 Have you ever had a nickname? What was it?

1736 What's been the highlight of your month so far?

1737 Who was the last person you high-fived?

1738 You receive a package. It has the correct address but the name's unfamiliar and there's no return address. What do you do?

1739 Which comedy duo is your all-time favorite?

1740 When you were growing up, what made you think your parents really did have eyes in the back of their head?

1741 If you could change three things about your life, what would they be?

1742 What are you so spectacularly bad at doing that it's almost impressive?

1743 Do you agree that there's no place like home?

1744 What was the last thing you got into an argument about?

1745 It's karaoke time! What will you sing?

1746 Which member of your family is the worst driver?

1747 If you could only keep one of the chairs you have at home, which one would it be, and why?

1748 What food or drink did your mom always make for you when you were sick?

1749 You step out of the shower and there's no towel. What do you use to dry yourself?

1750 When was the last time something happened that made you think *it's a small world*?

1751 What line from a movie do you like to use?

1752 Have you ever had a pen pal? Where did they live?

1753 What's your top tip for getting pets (or children) to take medication they refuse to take?

1754 If you were knocked unconscious at home, how long would it be before someone found you?

1755 What truth do you never want to know?

1756 Are video assistant referees ruining sports action?

1757 What life skill should all high school students be taught?

1758 You're writing a children's book about the adventures of a hen. What will you name the hen?

1759 What one piece of advice have you been given that you've passed on to others?

1760 Have you heard of Carhenge? What other items could you make into a Stonehenge replica?

1761 What footprints would you least like to see outside your tent in the morning?

1762 If you had your own country, what would you call your currency?

1763 What do you think is "so last year"?

1764 You suspect someone you know is involved in a crime. Would you report them to the police?

1765 Who was the last person you had a staring contest with? Did you win?

1766 What animal and its attributes would you like to add to the Chinese zodiac?

1767 How often do you change your phone case?

1768 What's been your hardest goodbye?

1769 Has there ever been a fashion trend you wouldn't wear because you looked ridiculous?

1770 What's your top tip for cleaning windows without leaving streaks?

1771 If not Gorilla Glue, what other animal might be a good match for the product?

1772 What TV show do you plan your day around to be able to watch it live?

1773 Do you agree that you can "never say never"?

1774 Who is the biggest hypochondriac you know, and what's the craziest disease they thought they had?

1775 Where's the most haunted-looking house you've ever seen?

1776 If you could change the sound of police sirens to something more fun for a day, what sound would you choose?

1777 What are you very enthusiastic about that those around you find dull?

1778 Have you ever had a personal trainer? What would your goal be if you had one?

1779 What fruit juice combination would you like to create and what would you call it?

1780 If you had your own TV show, what would the theme song be?

1781 What posters did you have on your bedroom wall when you were growing up?

1782 You have a pimple on the end of your nose. Do you squeeze it?

1783 What do you think happened to Amelia Earhart?

1784 If you were Mr. Potato Head, which attachments would suit your mood today?

1785 Can you create an armpit fart, and can you play a tune?

1786 What are your ASMR (brain massage) triggers?

1787 How many animals can you name that begin with the letter R?

1788 Where would you say your happy place is?

1789 What gadget from a sci-fi movie would be the coolest to have?

1790 If you could only listen to one song for the rest of the week, what would it be?

1791 What was the last thing you had to apologize to someone for?

1792 Do you know anyone who was named after a famous person?

1793   What one thing can no one make like your mama used to make it?

1794   Have you ever had a pillow fight? When was the last time?

1795   If not like a rocket, how do you move when you're running as fast as possible?

1796   "Don't be evil" is Google's official motto. What alternative motto would you give the company?

1797   What are your thoughts on euthanasia? Should it be legal?

1798   You're writing a crime novel. In what ingenious way does the murderer poison the victims?

1799   What do you think is the secret behind the *Mona Lisa's* smile?

1800   Have you ever closed your eyes and stuck a pin in a map to choose your vacation destination? Would you?

1801   What TV show do you prefer to watch on your own, and why?

1802   If you have a dishwasher, do you always stack it in a precise way?

1803   What's your top tip for avoiding tears when chopping onions?

1804   How different would your life be without Post-it Notes?

1805   What had you done the last time someone said they were disappointed in you?

1806   Where would you most like to be given a private guided tour?

1807   What would you not do, even if you were offered $10 million to do it?

1808   You wake up on the day of your wedding and can't go through with it. What do you do?

1809   What's the weirdest sports superstition or locker-room ritual you've heard of?

1810   Should people be allowed to keep any treasure they find?

1811   What lesson in life have you had to learn the hard way?

1812   Is your life today better than life was for your parents at the same age?

1813   What would be the funniest name for a new driving school?

1814   If you could only say one word for the rest of the day, what would you like that word to be?

1815   What's something you once thought only you knew, then you discovered everyone knew?

1816   There's a toilet museum in South Korea. What's the weirdest museum you've visited or heard of?

1817   Which creepy movie has the creepiest music?

1818   What would be a great new costume idea for The Masked Singer?

1819   When was the last time something totally unexpected happened to you, and what was it?

1820   If you have to pick a number between one and ten, do you always pick the same one?

1821   What are your thoughts on car eyelashes?

1822   Does life begin at forty?

1823   What were you doing the last time you gave up and stopped doing it?

1824   Who was the last person you called instead of texting or messaging?

1825   If not Rachel, Monica, Phoebe, Ross, Chandler, and Joey, what names should the characters of Friends have?

1826   What large animal would be the cutest if it became the size of a mouse?

1827   Have you ever had a tick? Do you know how to remove one?

1828   What do you think is the secret ingredient in Coca-Cola?

1829   Do you know anyone with more than one middle name? Who do you know with the longest full name?

1830   What song has been ruined by being used in a commercial?

1831   When you were a teenager, what were the coolest kids into?

1832   If you have a bucket list, do you add new things as others are achieved?

1833 What should happen to your belongings after you die?

1834 Have you ever had a wish come true? What was it?

1835 Where would you like to go on your honeymoon (or second honeymoon)?

1836 What's one thing not very many people know about you?

1837 If you were part of a Russian doll (nesting doll), which layer of the doll would you want to be?

1838 What's your top three list of the cutest animals in the world?

1839 Do you sing out loud when you're listening to music?

1840 Which TV show is the most overrated?

1841 You're under threat at home. What do you grab to defend yourself with?

1842 What new musical instrument could you invent by combining three existing instruments, and what would you call it?

1843 Is there something you've done that you would strongly advise others not to do, and what is it?

1844 What's the weirdest road sign you've ever seen?

1845 Have you ever had an imaginary friend? If you had one now, what would their name be?

1846 What have you discovered recently that more people should know about?

1847 Who was the last person to ruin your day and how?

1848 What potentially life-threatening allergy would you least like to have?

1849 You will be spending your next birthday alone. Will you celebrate it?

1850 What animal and sound would you like to add to "Old MacDonald Had a Farm"?

1851 If not white stripes on black, what color should pedestrian crosswalks be?

1852 What one thing can you say with absolute certainty you will never own?

1853 How many addresses have you lived at?

1854   What movie remake should never have been made?

1855   If you could only see shades of gray and one color, which one color would you want it to be?

1856   What was the last thing you had to leave work (or school) early for?

1857   Who is the biggest IT dinosaur you know?

1858   What's the saddest sound?

1859   If you could change the color of the sky from blue to any other color, which would you choose?

1860   What's Rodin's *The Thinker* thinking about?

1861   How often do you change your screensaver and what is it right now?

1862   What are your three favorite things about where you live?

1863   If you have a fly in your home, do you get rid of it? if so, how?

1864   What habits could you not tolerate a roommate having?

1865   You have a private island. What do you call it?

1866   What's your stock response to the question "How are you?"?

1867   Did you have a time-out spot in your home, and did you go there often?

1868   What kitchen gadget that used to be all the rage no longer exists?

1869   Have you binged on a box set recently? Which one?

1870   What do you think lies at the bottom of the Oak Island Money Pit?

1871   Do you find it easy to make new friends?

1872   What's the weirdest thing money can buy?

1873   Have you ever had something run out of battery at an inconvenient time? What was it?

1874   What was the last thing you heard or saw that made you roll your eyes?

1875   If you could change the outcome of one big event in history, what would it be?

1876   What fitness-wear fashion do you hope never comes back around?

1877   When you show your true colors, what colors are these?

1878   Andy Warhol had twenty-five cats named Sam. What would you call your twenty-five cats?

1879   What's the ultimate rich-boy's toy?

1880   Who was the last person to give you a wedgie? When and where?

1881   How often do you jump to conclusions without knowing all the facts?

1882   What movie title would be funniest if the word "die" was replaced with "dance"?

1883   You're trapped in your car in a snowstorm. What do you do?

1884   What six famous people (past or present) would make the most boring dinner party guests?

1885   If you could only speak the truth for a day, who would you try to avoid?

1886   What new pasta shape would you like to see introduced?

1887   When was the last time that you had to admit you were wrong, and why?

1888   What do you think the world's population will be in the year 2090?

1889   Have you heard of Dog Bark Park Inn or The Big Duck? What other oversized thing could you make into a building?

1890   What TV show theme song from long ago remains the most memorable for you?

1891   How do you behave when you lose your temper?

1892   What job from the past that no longer exists would you like to have tried?

1893   You work on the hundredth floor of an office building and all elevators are out for a week. What do you do?

1894   What kind of tail would you like to have?

1895   If not Nemo, what would be a great name for a clown fish?

1896   What are your views on CCTV cameras in school classrooms?

1897   Does modern technology complicate life? Why and how?

1898   Which family member are you closest to, and has it always been this way?

1899   What's the worst part of having a cold?

1900   If you were presented with a music award, what genre of music would it be for?

1901   What movie is so spectacularly bad that it's almost good?

1902   Time is a great healer, but what can't it heal?

1903   What line would you like to add to the "Wheels on the Bus" song?

1904   Where would you like to be living in twenty years?

1905   What artificial fruit flavor is least like the real flavor?

1906   How often do you meet the five-a-day fruit and vegetable target, and how do you do it?

1907   What have you committed to doing to save the environment?

1908   Where will Banksy strike next?

1909   Have you ever considered yourself to be someone's number one fan? Whose?

1910   What do you think happened to the crew of the Mary Celeste?

1911   If you hyphenate the name of your first pet with your family name, what showbiz name do you get?

1912   What fruit do you always take from the bowl first?

1913   Should relationships always be prioritized over careers?

1914   What's the weirdest reason for a traffic hold-up you've come across?

1915   If you could only study three important subjects to learn at school, what would they be?

1916   What precious possession would you be most sad about if you broke it?

1917   Do you find it hard to talk about death in your family?

1918   What was the last thing you learned how to do by watching YouTube?

1919   How often do you wash your jeans?

1920   What are your views on animal testing in scientific research?

1921   Have you heard of International Talk Like a Pirate Day? What international day would you like to create?

1922   What's your star sign and do you have the associated character traits?

1923   If you inherited five hundred acres of land, what would you do with it?

1924   What kitchen gadget do you have that you never use?

1925   Did you ever dream of marrying a fictional character? Which one?

1926   What do you think would happen if you fell into a black hole?

1927   You're the ruler of a brand-new country. What colors and design will you choose for your national flag?

1928   What's the worst job in the world?

1929   Have you ever had to chase after something that got blown away in the wind? What was it?

1930   What animal looks way too cute to be as deadly as it is?

1931   Help! There's no toilet paper! What do you use instead?

1932   Who is the funniest comedian of all time?

1933   What one thing can you say with certainty you will never do?

1934   You're a boxing champion. What music accompanies you into the ring?

1935   What's your spaghetti eating technique?

1936   Is there something you're good at but you'd rather not be?

1937 What are your views on facial recognition technology in schools and on the street?

1938 Have you ever ridden a horse? Where and when?

1939 What would your pirate name be?

1940 You have a six-hour delay at the airport before your next flight. How do you pass the time?

1941 If not the "big bad wolf," what other animal should have been big and bad in fairy tales?

1942 What do you usually share on social media?

1943 Does there need to be evidence before something can be a truth?

1944 What's the most unusual building material you could use to build a house?

1945 Where were you when you were the coldest you've ever been?

1946 If not you, which one of your friends eats a KitKat in the most annoying way?

1947 What TV show would you get bored with fastest if it was the only one you could watch?

1948 Do you fit the stereotypical image of someone from your country? In what way?

1949 What kind of earphones do you prefer and why?

1950 Have you ever had to evacuate a building because the fire alarm went off?

1951 Did you have a favorite place to go when you were a kid, and when did you last go there?

1952 What do you wish could be recycled?

1953 If you could organize a good deed project in your neighborhood, what would it be?

1954 What made-up word would you like to see added to the dictionary?

1955 When was the last time you agreed with the statement "less is more"?

1956   What person from history would you most like to have shaken hands with? Why?

1957   If you were Puss in Boots, what style of boots would you wear?

1958   Have you ever had to fish something out of the trash? What was it?

1959   Is there something you do in a quirky way compared to other people?

1960   What aspect of life before the internet do you find hardest to imagine (or remember if you were there)?

1961   At five foot eight you'd be the height of a London black cab. What can you compare your height to?

1962   If not you, who or what has this been an amazing week for?

1963   Which famous person attracts the worst type of fan?

1964   When you meet friends in a coffee shop, do you always sit at the same table? Why?

1965   If you knew you wouldn't get caught, would you break the law, and which law would you break?

1966   What song from a musical did you last sing, and what were you doing at the time?

1967   How often do you connect with nature? How?

1968   What do you wish people wouldn't eat on the street?

1969   You're the owner of a company famed for its funky packaging. What makes it funky?

1970   What was the last thing you made up an excuse to get out of doing?

1971   Have you ever had to put someone into the recovery position? Do you know how to do it?

1972   What thoughts have been at the forefront of your mind today?

1973   If you could own a famous work of art, what would you choose?

1974   What TV show's final episode was the biggest disappointment to you?

1975 You're a famous pop star known by just one name. What is it?

1976 What will be the next big scientific breakthrough?

1977 Who should have a star on Hollywood's Walk of Fame?

1978 Do you agree that sorry is the hardest word?

1979 Where were you when you saw the prettiest sunset?

1980 What one thing could you change to start saving money?

1981 If you were reincarnated as a non-living thing, what would you want to be?

1982 What aspect of your country's heritage are you most interested in preserving?

1983 Have you ever completely lost track of time? What were you doing?

1984 What parenting behaviors do you believe negatively affects children?

1985 What would be an awesome supermarket own-brand copycat name for Pop-Tarts?

1986 If you could change one thing about the last hour, what would you change?

1987 Tom Hanks and Ozzy Osbourne arrive at your door in a hurry. What do they want?

1988 Can you do mental arithmetic?

1989 What's your opinion on arranged marriages?

1990 If you were starving, would you eat roadkill?

1991 What were you into as a teenager that you thought you'd always be into but then lost interest?

1992 Have you ever had to return a meal served to you in a restaurant? Why?

1993 What product name would you give to the opposite of Gorilla Glue?

1994 If you lived in Candyland, what would you like trees to be made of?

1995 What's the most distant place from your home that you've visited?

1996 How often do you listen to classical music and who is your favorite composer?

1997 What technology will replace smart phones?

1998 Should schools have classroom pets?

1999 What do you wish you could bottle?

2000 Do you agree that you can have too much of a good thing? Have you experienced it?

2001 What's the weirdest load you've seen on the back of a truck?

2002 If one color had to be removed from the rainbow, which one should it be?

2003 What's your opinion of people who wear shades indoors?

2004 Have you ever had to wear a uniform to work (school), and what was it?

2005 What tastes weird after eating a mint?

2006 If you could be world champion at something, what would it be?

2007 What app do you open most on an average day?

2008 Who is the greatest person to have ever lived?

2009 What style of hat suits you best?

2010 You have acquired a racehorse. What will you name it?

2011 What would you say to someone if you really wanted to confuse them?

2012 If you could own any type of car, what would you choose?

2013 You're the maker of world-famous pies with a secret ingredient. What is that secret ingredient?

2014 Who should be the next James Bond?

2015 Author Roald Dahl created alien creatures called "vermicious knids." What alien creature name can you think up?

2016 What assumptions have people made about you that are totally wrong?

2017 How do you eat an Oreo?

2018 What studio audience would you most like to be in?

2019 Where was the last place you traveled to by bus and did you talk to any other passengers?

2020 What Jell-O flavor should be introduced?

2021 Is there something you know about someone that they don't know you know?

2022 What still-to-be-written bestseller would you like to be the author of?

2023 When you get a gut feeling or hunch about something, are you usually right?

2024 What's the first sign of madness?

2025 If you lost your phone, how many phone numbers would you know by heart?

2026 What would your friends say you're a little snobbish about?

2027 When was the last time you asked someone for directions?

2028 What stereotypical belief about your country is not true?

2029 You're a fearless BASE jumper. What landmark or building will you jump from next?

2030 What do you wish you could do every day?

2031 Have you ever had your mind blown by a logic puzzle? What was it?

2032 What item of clothing would you rather die than be seen wearing in public?

2033 If you were required by law to have a body piercing, what would you pierce?

2034 What would your day be like if you switched places with your pet?

2035 Which products have the weirdest TV commercials?

2036 What was the last thing you overreacted to and blew up out of proportion?

2037 How many 1980s pop stars can you name?

2038 What's your main goal in life?

2039 If one of your internal organs had to be external, which one would you want it to be?

2040 What stage show would you most like to get tickets for?

2041 Have you ever had, or would you consider having cosmetic surgery?

2042 What's your most ridiculous "first world problem"?

2043 How often do you step outside of your comfort zone? When was the last time?

2044 What TV-show kitchen would you most like to have?

2045 If you could plant a tree in your garden, what type would you choose?

2046 What's the bravest thing you've ever done?

2047 Do you have a birthmark on your body? Where is it?

2048 What's the weirdest pregnancy craving you've ever heard of?

2049 If you could be the drummer in a band, which one would it be?

2050 What one thing do people procrastinate over more than anything else?

2051 Have you heard of Klingon and Na'vi? What fictional or constructed language would you like to be able to speak?

2052 What do you wish you'd invented?

2053 If you lost your sense of smell, what smell would you miss most?

2054 Which famous person is the exact opposite of you?

2055 How old do people think you are?

2056 What sport requires the highest level of fitness?

2057 If Peter Rabbit had to be renamed, what would you call him?

2058 What was the last thing you pinned on your fridge door?

2059 Did you give your first car a name (or what would you name your first car)?

2060   What spam email do you receive most often?

2061   Where was the last place you stayed on a family vacation?

2062   What job would you like to be able to do but know you wouldn't be any good at?

2063   You're the host of a new daytime talk show. Who is your first guest?

2064   What sound would you like to have as a doorbell?

2065   If you could change one thing you did or said today, what would it be?

2066   What's your most enduring pet peeve?

2067   Have you dressed up for World Book Day? What book character would you dress as now?

2068   What do you yell when you're in a location with an echo?

2069   Do you know how to change a lightbulb, and when did you last do it?

2070   What's the biggest difference in culture between North America and the United Kingdom?

2071   If you met an alien, what would you say?

2072   What sound should a reversing truck make to ensure everyone gets out of the way?

2073   You're a human by day and another creature by night. What other creature would you be?

2074   Who or what were you into last year that you're so not into this year?

2075   What item in your fridge today has been in there the longest?

2076   Under what circumstances are you most impatient?

2077   What song of today will be a golden oldie twenty years from now?

2078   If you could change a fictional story line so a character wouldn't die, which story line would it be?

2079   Have you ever haggled for a better deal? Were you successful?

2080 What's your kryptonite?

2081 How do you celebrate Independence Day and do you do the same every year?

2082 What twenty-first-century expression is a good update for "burning the candle at both ends"?

2083 If you could replace the Mount Rushmore heads with those of four people in your life, whose would you choose?

2084 Should students be allowed to choose which books they read in English classes?

2085 What awkward happening have you had to style your way out of recently?

2086 Does opportunity only ever knock once?

2087 What's your favorite Starbucks drink and why?

2088 If you were the BFG, what dream would you like to bottle?

2089 What was the last thing you read out loud, and why?

2090 Have you heard of Moonpig? What would you name your rival online greeting cards business?

2091 Who is the greatest sportsperson of all time, and why?

2092 Is there something you do (or don't do) that other people find hard to understand or accept?

2093 What song makes you feel like dancing every time you hear it?

2094 When was the last time you ate a panini and what filling did you have?

2095 You have been asked to name a new super-powerful firework. What will you name it?

2096 What are fishing garden gnomes fishing for?

2097 If you could roar like a lion, when would you do it to have the biggest impact?

2098 What's the best thing about getting older?

2099 When you flip a coin to choose between two options, do you always make the same call?

2100 What does "a life well lived" mean to you?

2101 You're starting a new blog. What's it about and what will you call it?

2102 Which famous person would you most like to go shopping with?

2103 What's your favorite Super Bowl food? What items should you always have on a Super Bowl party menu?

2104 If you must lose all memories of your life except one, which one would you want to keep?

2105 What's your idea of a perfect TV dinner?

2106 Which profession today is no longer as respected as it once was?

2107 How do you hide your emotions?

2108 What was the last thing you said to yourself inside your head?

2109 Could you talk someone through how to tie a shoelace without using your hands to demonstrate?

2110 What should go on the top of a Christmas tree?

2111 How old does an item need to be before you consider it to be a "vintage" piece?

2112 What one thing do you do to reduce the level of stress in your day?

2113 Have you ever howled at the moon?

2114 Where was the last place you got stuck for hours and thought you'd die of boredom?

2115 What's the best feeling in the world?

2116 If one letter had to go missing from your keyboard, which one would you like it to be?

2117 What routine medical examination do you dread most?

2118 Who or what was the last thing you physically applauded?

2119 Beyond spending, what other things have you done with your pennies?

2120 Have you (or do you) organized your pens or crayons by color?

2121 What's the weirdest item you've heard of someone shoplifting?

2122 If you could be the opposite sex for one day, what would you want to do?

2123 What two famous stage names can be combined to create an awesome new stage name?

2124 What was your lowest performing subject at school? Did you ever fail a subject?

2125 What one question do you hope no one ever asks you?

2126 Where was the biggest waterfall you ever saw?

2127 What old-fashioned baby name is least likely to come back into fashion?

2128 Have you ever checked under the bed before getting into it? What were you checking for?

2129 What baby animal do you find the most adorable?

2130 If you were the fashion police, what item of clothing would you ban forever?

2131 What noise would make a hilarious car horn?

2132 How old were you when you had the best birthday cake ever?

2133 If you could see behind the scenes, which celebrity would be the most boring when not performing?

2134 What does "dress to kill" mean to you, and what did you wear last time you did it?

2135 Do you have a favorite Christmas movie that you watch every year?

2136 What one thing do you need to get done today?

2137 You're a karate chop superstar. What amazing item can you split in half?

2138 What musical instrument is the coolest to play?

2139 Who or what was the last thing that intimidated you?

2140 Have you ever hurt or broken a tooth biting into something, and what was it?

2141 Where's the most exotic place anyone could spend their childhood years?

2142 What mispronunciation irks you or makes you laugh the most?

2143 If one part of your body could be detachable, which part would you choose?

2144 Would you sell a kidney if you needed the money?

2145 If you could be the face of a brand or product, what would it be?

2146 What's your hometown most famous for?

2147 You're Simon Cowell and you're creating a new boy band. What will it be called?

2148 What's the best age to get married?

2149 Have you ever been totally prepared for something, only to discover you were prepared on the wrong day?

2150 What one film have you not seen that it seems everyone else in the world has seen?

2151 If pets gave their owners names, which three names would be most popular?

2152 Is there something we believe to be a fact today that will turn out not to be?

2153 Under what circumstances will you give up your seat to someone else on crowded public transport?

2154 What was the last thing you saw or heard that made your jaw drop?

2155 How do you like to eat a Twizzler?

2156 If you could send a message in a bottle right now, what would it be?

2157 What line would you like to add to the "If You're Happy and You Know It" song?

2158 When was the last time you ate your all-time favorite food?

2159 If you were the star of a show, who or what would your sidekick be?

2160 What does a perfect Sunday afternoon look like for you?

2161 Do you agree that some questions are best left unanswered? Which ones?

2162 What mind-blowing statistics do you know?

2163 Have you ever judged a book by its cover and found you were wrong?

2164 Where's your tickle spot and what happens if someone finds it?

2165 You're a sculptor and you've been commissioned to create a piece for your town center. What will it be?

2166 What bad omens do you believe in?

2167 Earth, air, fire, water: do you know which astrological element you are?

2168 What movie did someone spoil for you by telling you the ending?

2169 If you need to lift a friend's spirits, what do you do?

2170 What two important things did your mom teach you?

2171 You have broken both arms and need help to eat. What food would you not want to be fed?

2172 What's your go-to non-cuss word if you drop something on your toe?

2173 Who is the humblest person you know?

2174 If you could shapeshift into three things, what would those things be?

2175 What playground games did you play as a kid?

2176 Where is the most beautiful beach you've visited?

2177 What's Switzerland most famous for?

2178 Should the baggage allowance on flights include the weight of the passenger?

2179 Which fictional baddie is the "baddest" of them all?

2180 What are some unwritten rules in society today?

2181 If rain could have a flavor, what would you want it to be?

2182 What one thing do you need to make your life easier?

2183 Have you bought an item recently that you had to return? What was it and why?

2184 When you close your eyes, what can you see?

2185 If red wasn't hot and blue wasn't cold, what colors should be used as indicators?

2186 What does being "outdoorsy" mean to you?

2187 How old were you when you had your first coffee?

2188 What's the weirdest item you've absentmindedly put in totally the wrong place?

2189 If you were to be buried with items you might need in the afterlife, what three items would you choose?

2190 What promise have you made and then broken?

2191 You're setting up a new picture framing business. What will you call it?

2192 Who or what was the last person or thing to make you feel angry?

2193 Are you able to say no, even when it will make you unpopular?

2194 What was the last thing you saw that made you feel squeamish?

2195 If scientists discovered a way to travel through time and the death rate was one in one million, would you travel?

2196 What boo-boo from your childhood can you still remember today?

2197 Do you agree with Andy Warhol that everyone gets fifteen minutes of fame?

2198 What does Christmas mean to you?

2199 How old were you when you had your first crush, and who was it?

2200 What band or singer that no longer tours would you most like to have seen perform live?

2201 If snow could fall in three different colors, which ones would you choose, and why?

2202 What nursery/kindergarten song would sound cool as a heavy metal song?

2203 Where is the happiest place on the planet?

2204 Have you ever jumped into water fully clothed?

2205 Where's the weirdest place someone might have been when they heard JFK was shot?

2206 Can you say, "How much wood would a woodchuck chuck if a woodchuck could chuck wood?" in full?

2207 What belief do you have that other people find weird?

2208 If you could be invisible for one hour, where would you go? And what would you do?

2209 What's your favorite zoo animal?

2210 You're about to plant a vegetable garden. What's the first thing you want to grow?

2211 What's one important life lesson you've learned?

2212 Have you ever knowingly bought a fake designer item? What was it?

2213 What music track would you play on a loop to get rid of everyone at the end of a house party?

2214 Is there something about your physical appearance that you try to hide or disguise? What is it?

2215 What two names should parents not be allowed to name their children?

2216 How do you pass the time when you're waiting in a long line for a theme park ride?

2217 If someone else had to make all your decisions for you, who would you want it to be?

2218 When was the last time you attended a wedding and did everything run smoothly?

2219 What's fun as a spectator but not as a participant?

2220 If you needed a watertight alibi for your whereabouts last night, who would give it?

2221 Which book should everyone read at least once?

2222 Did you ever try to find the pot of gold at the end of the rainbow?

2223 What movie would you watch if you wanted to have a good cry?

2224 Who is your favorite Ninja Turtle?

2225 Where's the safest place to stand if you're outdoors in a lightning storm?

2226 If someone offered you a million dollars for your super-affectionate pet cat, would you take it?

2227 What bionic body part would you most like to have?

2228 You're running for your life and leap over a wall. What do you hope is on the other side?

2229 Where's the best seat in the cinema?

2230 Have you ever knowingly broken a law?

2231 What brand of chocolate do you prefer and why?

2232 If your sense of smell was ten million times stronger for one day, where would you avoid going?

2233 What pseudoscience annoys you most and why?

2234 Who is your biggest hero?

2235 How would the Teenage Mutant Ninja Turtles series be different if the turtles were middle-aged?

2236 What was the last thing you stapled together?

2237 If you could be a teacher of anything, what would it be?

2238 What one thing do you regret not doing?

2239 What's the weirdest interior or theme you've heard of a restaurant having?

2240 If you needed glasses or new frames, what style would you choose?

2241 What's a recipe for disaster?

2242   You have five hundred emails and no time to open them all. How do you decide which ones to open first?

2243   What BMX jump is the coolest?

2244   What's your favorite word to describe someone who is drunk?

2245   If you could sit on any sofa featured in a movie or TV show, which one would it be?

2246   What music at your funeral would make your loved ones laugh?

2247   Who do you want to save the last dance for?

2248   When you achieve a goal, do you always set another one?

2249   If you were to shrink an inch every time you checked your phone today, how tall would you be by bedtime?

2250   You're all out of salt and pepper. What do you use for seasoning?

2251   Who is the last person you would ask for fashion advice?

2252   Do you have a favorite meme? What is it?

2253   If something you'd borrowed from a friend got broken while you had it, what would you do?

2254   What one thing do you wish there was more of?

2255   Have you ever roasted chestnuts on an open fire, and when was the last time?

2256   What are some words or phrases that are unique to your town or region?

2257   If you needed to hide candy from someone at home, where would you put it?

2258   What two questions would you ask someone you just met to learn the most about them?

2259   Should the sale of dinosaur bones in auctions be stopped? Why?

2260   What does family mean to you?

2261   Which five people do you spend the most time with when you're not at work (school)?

2262 If someone says, "Don't look now . . ." do you always look?

2263 What bug would freak you out most if it landed on you?

2264 You're planning a first date. Where's a good place to go?

2265 What movie would have been better with a different actor in the lead role?

2266 Who or what makes you smile most?

2267 What's a good example you've seen of older not being wiser?

2268 If you were walking through a forest and suddenly saw a bear, what would you do?

2269 Where's the noisiest place you've been, and what was making the noise?

2270 How would you deal with an angry chihuahua refusing to let you enter a building?

2271 Where's the best place you ever found to hide in a game of hide-and-seek?

2272 Is there one thing your parents did that you said you will never do?

2273 What does fresh air smell like?

2274 Do you agree with big game hunting? Why?

2275 What shoes or boots featured in a movie would you most like to try wearing?

2276 Have you ever borrowed something and not given it back? What was it?

2277 What's your favorite word or phrase for breaking wind?

2278 If you could snap your fingers and change one thing about yourself, what would it be?

2279 You're an award-winning dancer. What type of dance do you do?

2280 What was the last thing you started and then wished you hadn't?

2281 A hypnotist has convinced you that you can only move by hopping like a kangaroo. What's the toughest part of your day?

2282 What business should provide a drive-thru service?

2283　Have you ever laughed so hard a little bit of pee came out? When?

2284　What punishment should dog owners be given for not picking up dog poop?

2285　If you needed to pick a lock, what item that you carry with you would you try using first?

2286　How would you describe a stereotypical Australian?

2287　Where do you hide important or valuable documents in your home?

2288　What's a fair way to split household chores?

2289　Do you have a favorite mug? If so, why is it your favorite?

2290　If you could be someone's pet for a day, who would it be, and what would you be?

2291　Have you ever run out of fuel in your car? What did you do (or what would you do)?

2292　When was the last time you blushed and why?

2293　What movie scene still makes you emotional no matter how many times you see it?

2294　How would you describe an elf?

2295　What two slightly more out of the ordinary things "go together like a horse and carriage"?

2296　If someone wants to know what kind of music you're into, what answer do you give?

2297　Did you ever tease or bully anyone at school?

2298　If Santa had an extra reindeer, what would its name be?

2299　Which word in the English language is the most beautiful?

2300　Have you ever accidentally dropped something into the toilet and had to fish it out? What was it?

2301　If you were Willy Wonka, what candy would you invent next?

2302　What's your favorite weather?

2303 How would you describe the color of a perfect slice of toast?

2304 What one thing do you wish you had a dollar for every time it happened?

2305 If someone said they would buy your ticket, would you sign up for space tourism?

2306 What does happiness smell like?

2307 You're asked what your name means. What imaginative but ultimately fake answer could you give?

2308 Do you have a guilty pleasure and are you willing to own up to it?

2309 What breed of dog is the most ridiculous?

2310 If you could start a business tomorrow, what would it be?

2311 What should be the next hands-free gadget?

2312 Where do you display the most fragile ornament or trinket in your home?

2313 You're out of sugar and you need it for the recipe you're making. What do you use instead?

2314 When was the last time you yelled at the TV or radio? What about?

2315 You have no corkscrew. How will you open a corked bottle?

2316 What two savory foods wouldn't taste better with a little cheese grated on top?

2317 If Sir Walter Raleigh hadn't introduced potatoes to Europe, what other discovery might he have introduced?

2318 What should the buttons on a gingerbread man should be made of?

2319 If you could be an elite athlete in any sport, which would it be?

2320 What's the weirdest impulse buy you've ever made?

2321 If you no longer needed to go to work, what would you do with your life?

2322 Who is the last person you'd call for help solving a crossword puzzle clue?

2323 What was the last thing you stitched by hand?

2324 Which type of chocolate in a box is your least favorite, but you'll eat it anyway?

2325 Have you ever left the key for the door under the mat?

2326 What buzzwords do you find most annoying?

2327 How do you like to eat a crème egg?

2328 If someone you knew was having a panic attack, what would you do to help them?

2329 What's your favorite way to mix the topping of your frozen yoghurt?

2330 As nervous as a long tail cat in a room full of rocking chairs. What's your favorite nervous simile?

2331 What are sweet dreams made of?

2332 Is there one person you would give your life to save? Who?

2333 What's "the best thing since sliced bread"?

2334 If Star Wars had to be renamed, what would be a good alternative?

2335 What smell always makes you feel hungry?

2336 Should the world be more respectful to politicians?

2337 What does living an "ordinary" life mean to you?

2338 If someone else's life depended on it, could you face your greatest fear?

2339 You're creating a new kids' wear brand. What will you call it?

2340 Which food do you think is the noisiest to eat?

2341 If you witnessed a mugging, what would you do?

2342 How would you describe the feeling of an ice-cream brain freeze?

2343 What caged animal would you least like to clean up after?

2344 Which X-Men mutation would you most like to have?

2345 Have you ever changed a car tire, or would you know how to do it if you had to?

2346 What question have you only given a half-truthful answer to recently?

2347 If you could start a magazine, what would it be about?

2348 You're on the Star Trek *Enterprise* and you discover a new life form. What name will you give it?

2349 What two things (could be anything) would you swap to cause the greatest chaos?

2350 Do you agree that there's a place for everything and everything has its place?

2351 What incurable disease would you most like to discover a cure for?

2352 When was the last time you built a sandcastle?

2353 How would you describe the texture of a mushroom to someone who's never seen or eaten one?

2354 What does success look like?

2355 If you could ask your great-grandparents one question, what would it be?

2356 What's your favorite video game sport to play?

2357 Have you ever lied about what you do for a job? Why?

2358 What small animal would look the most awesome if it became the size of an elephant?

2359 When was the last time you were on a playground roundabout and did you play dangerous games on it?

2360 You're directly in the path of fast-flowing lava. How will you escape it?

2361 What one thing gets an unnecessary amount of hate?

2362 If the best things in life are free, what are they?

2363 How would you describe the feeling of being hungry?

2364 What's the weirdest hiccup cure you've ever heard of?

2365 If you could start a new trend, what would it be?

2366 Can you do a "live long and prosper" Vulcan hand greeting like Spock?

2367 What bug would you least like your home to be infested with?

2368 How would you describe your relationship with money?

2369 What camouflage colors would you need to be able to hide from predators in your daily environment?

2370 If you could suddenly fly, where would you go first?

2371 What song from a Disney movie sticks in your head most?

2372 Where do all the missing socks go?

2373 Have you ever said "hi" to someone on the street thinking it was someone else?

2374 What was the last thing you stuck your finger in?

2375 Which two fictional characters would have the most awesome baby if they got together?

2376 Do you agree that nothing in life is simple? Why?

2377 What ingredients should go into the ultimate one-pot meal?

2378 Have you ever lied about your age? When? Why?

2379 "I would do anything for love, but I won't do that," sang Meatloaf. What wouldn't you do for love?

2380 What's your favorite version of the poem that begins "roses are red"?

2381 Is there one color of clothing you own more of than any other? What is it?

2382 What thing did you ask Santa for more than once but never got?

2383 You have no matches or lighters. How will you light the barbecue?

2384 What dog breed should win all canine beauty contests?

2385 How do you make sure you don't forget to do something important?

2386 You're on the first floor of a store when an earthquake hits. What do you do?

2387 If you could add one more color to the rainbow, what would it be?

2388 What two things do you always keep by your bed at night?

2389 Have you ever climbed a tree, and if so, when was the last time you did it?

2390 Who is the loudest snorer you know?

2391 What was the last card game you played?

2392 If the Clue (Cluedo) characters were real people, who would be most likely to get away with murder?

2393 If you only had one day left to live, what would you have for your last meal?

2394 Does stepping into a position of power change people?

2395 You're creating a photo calendar. What photo do you use for October?

2396 Have you ever accidentally-on-purpose broken something because you hated it? What was it?

2397 What tense drama would be funniest if turned into a musical?

2398 When's the last time you lied to your parents and why?

2399 Which *Harry Potter* character would you least like to be sitting next to on a long-haul flight?

2400 What are the biggest challenges young people face today?

2401 Have you ever been to a school reunion?

2402 Where are you from? Is it where you call home now?

2403 If you see a "wet paint" sign, do you touch the paint to see if it really is wet?

2404 When was the last time you couldn't get to sleep? What did you do?

2405 What radio jingle sticks in your mind most?

2406 If you could swap bodies with someone for a day, who would it be?

2407 Do you agree with Malcolm Gladwell's 10,000-Hour Rule, and that deliberate practice leads to expertise in anything?

2408 Which two colors would you never wear together?

2409 What can you do that other people think you can't do?

2410 Should theaters be more relaxed, and would you take your shoes off in one?

2411 What incredible fact do you find it most difficult to get your head around?

2412 If you suddenly became deaf, what sound would you miss most?

2413 What's your favorite version of "keep calm and carry on"?

2414 How would you design a spice rack for a blind person?

2415 What was the last thing you thought was "a sight for sore eyes"?

2416 If the Pied Piper could lead more than rats away, what one other animal do you wish had followed him?

2417 What things about life today will people be nostalgic about in thirty years' time?

2418 Have you ever lit a campfire? Would you know how?

2419 What can you never have enough of?

2420 If you could switch the sounds two animals make, what two would make the funniest switch?

2421 What one thing have you seen that you wish you never had?

2422 You're on a sightseeing tour and notice your guide's zipper is down. What do you do?

2423 At what age does a person become "elderly"?

2424 Who is one of the most intelligent people you know personally? Do you ask them for information or advice?

2425 What canapés or finger foods should be banned from formal parties?

2426 Have you ever literally danced the night away? What type of dance were you doing?

2427 What was the last dance move you learned?

2428 If you could taste a rainbow, what would indigo taste like?

2429 What two things do you most like about your job (or school)?

2430 You're entering a best-dressed scarecrow competition. What clothes will you use?

2431 When you're going on vacation, when do you pack your suitcases?

2432 How would you explain what a meme is to someone who has no idea?

2433 Is there no such thing as a free lunch?

2434 When was the last time you were late for something? What was it?

2435 What was the last food you really craved?

2436 If you could ask Walt Disney one question, what would it be?

2437 What's the weirdest food you've seen cooked on a barbecue?

2438 If you woke up inside the last video game you'd played, what would your chances of survival be?

2439 Where DNA is available, should extinct animals be brought back to life?

2440 What's your favorite type of takeaway food?

2441 Do you agree that some people are born evil?

2442 What was the last thing you thought was too good to be true?

2443 How low into the red will you let your fuel gauge go before you fill up?

2444 What cartoons do you still watch today?

2445 Do you tear Scotch tape with your teeth?

2446 Baby fat is sometimes called puppy fat. What would be a cute name for adult fat?

2447 You have one minute to make something out of an empty shoebox. What will you make?

2448 What donut topping or filling is your absolute favorite?

2449 How do you respond to unwanted advice?

2450 If you could add a made-up word to the dictionary, what would it be and what would it mean?

2451 What inanimate object in your home would you most like to have a conversation with?

2452 Have you ever drawn the short straw? What did you have to do?

2453 Where did you go the last time you had an "excellent adventure"?

2454 Do you agree with the ban on heading balls in youth soccer?

2455 Who is the most annoyingly cheerful person you know?

2456 What was the worst punishment you received for misbehaving as a child?

2457 If you could test drive any land vehicle, what would you choose?

2458 What celebrity death has made you emotional?

2459 You're lost in the woods and come to a fork in the path. How do you decide which path to take?

2460 If the answer is ten, what's the question?

2461 Which herbivore would be the scariest if it became a carnivore?

2462 Can you remember the title of the first book you read on your own?

2463 If you could trace your ancestry back to someone famous in history, who would you want it to be?

2464 When was the last time you couldn't read your own handwriting?

2465 You're forming a rock band. What will you call it?

2466 If you woke up tomorrow and discovered you had slept for ten years, what question would you ask first?

2467 What two things should people never Google?

2468 Have you ever blown a bubblegum bubble that burst all over your face?

2469 What reindeer games do you think Santa's reindeer play, and should Rudolph be allowed to join in?

2470 If the closest round object is the cause of your death, how do you die?

2471 What's your favorite type of puzzle?

2472 Did you ever have a flip phone? Do you miss it?

2473 What are the top three most used apps on your phone?

2474 When was the last time you wanted the ground to open up and swallow you?

2475 What cargo would be the worst truck spill on a highway?

2476 If the Incredible Hulk wasn't green, what color should he be?

2477 What image would make the toughest jigsaw puzzle?

2478 Have you ever locked the keys for something inside the something?

2479 What was the last thing you waited patiently for? Was it worth the wait?

2480 Do you have a home remedy that you swear by? What is it?

2481 What was your favorite breakfast cereal as a child? Do you still eat it now?

2482 When you were growing up, what job did you want to have?

2483 If you suddenly developed fabulous artistic ability, what would you like to create?

2484 What one thing is it impossible for anyone to look cool doing?

2485 Should there be a death penalty? Why?

2486 "I've been expecting you, Mr. Bond . . ." What funny scenario might Blofeld have been caught in had he not been expecting him?

2487 Is there life after death?

2488 What caused your most recent bruise?

2489 Have you ever looked at strangers around you and imagined their life story?

2490 What illness would you pretend to have if you wanted to get out of doing something?

2491 If you suddenly had an elephant's trunk, who would you spray with water first?

2492 What's your favorite tongue twister?

2493 Do you agree with the idea that you should do one thing every day that scares you?

2494 What's the weirdest exhibit you've heard of in an art gallery?

2495 You're jogging in the park and an aggressive loose dog chases after you. What do you do?

2496 Which two animals would you mix to make a new species?

2497 At what point in life did you know what you wanted to do when you grew up?

2498 What character flaw are you least tolerant of in others?

2499 Have you ever attended an event and felt totally over or underdressed? What was the event?

2500 What dream or nightmare have you had more than once?

2501 Which household chore do you least like doing?

2502 What helps to recharge you when you're lacking energy?

2503 Which TV show do you think should be more popular?

2504 If the Monopoly board featured your hometown, what two properties would be the most expensive to buy?

2505 What two words would your work (school) colleagues use to describe your character?

2506 What houseplant best suits your personality?

2507 What's the worst shopping experience you've ever had?

2508 Do you think cats and dogs understand us if we meow or bark?

2509 What weird place did you fit into as a child that you wish you could still fit into now?

2510 You're freaking out. What do you do to calm yourself down?

2511 If you and your friends had an apple throwing contest, who would throw the farthest?

2512 What character from a childhood book or movie did you connect with most?

2513 How would you go about explaining American football to someone who's never seen a game?

2514 What restaurant have you eaten at more than any other, and do you always order the same meal?

2515 If you could transport a very angry hippo into any point in history, where would you put it?

2516 You have ten seconds to name three hits by the Beatles. Can you do it?

2517 What's your favorite thing to make with bananas?

2518 Have you ever cheated in a game or a test, and did you get away with it?

2519 What was the last thing you were daydreaming about when you should have been paying attention to something else?

2520 If the red carpet wasn't red, what color should it be?

2521 During which medical procedure would you least like to wake up from the anesthetic?

2522 Which two colors do you think coordinate best with yellow?

2523 Have you ever looked in the mirror and not recognized yourself? When was this?

2524 What were you doing the last time you surprised yourself as well as others?

2525 When was the last time you couldn't stop yawning?

2526 If the sound of you coughing could be replaced with any sound effect, what sound would you choose?

2527 What color clothing doesn't suit you?

2528 When you were growing up, was there something in your home you were told you must not touch?

2529 Who is the most beautiful person you know?

2530 Is there is a job that one sex can do better than the other? What is it?

2531 What else happened in the world in the year you were born?

2532 You're invited to a themed party and must dress as a character from *Star Wars*. What will you wear?

2533 Which TV personality has a face that was meant for radio?

2534 If you wear shoes with laces, do you always untie them before you take them off?

2535 What's the weirdest food name you've heard?

2536 If you won a large sum of money in a charity prize draw, would you donate it to the charity?

2537 What idiom could be used as the opposite of "as the crow flies"?

2538 Do you always treat others the way you would wish to be treated yourself?

2539 What common expression do you find the most annoying when people use it?

2540 You're going away for a weekend break. Which three essentials would you pack?

2541 Have you ever bought anything at a garage sale? What?

2542 What's your favorite thing about being you?

2543 If the White House had to be a different color, what should it be?

2544 How would you politely deal with food that's too hot in your mouth without grossing everyone out?

2545 What emoji do you use most?

2546 If the Statue of Liberty wasn't holding a torch, what would you replace It with?

2547 What are the two most stereotypical North American names?

2548 If you see a big red button, do you want to touch it?

2549 Can you eat a donut without licking your lips?

2550 How long would your whiskers need to be if they were your guide to fitting your body through a space?

2551 What type of car sends out a message that you're doing well for yourself without flaunting it?

2552 If you could travel back in time, but you then had to stay there, would you go?

2553 What's your favorite song with a person's name in the title or lyrics?

2554 Do you agree that size doesn't matter?

2555 What character trait(s) have you inherited from your parents?

2556 If walls could talk, which walls would you like to have a conversation with?

2557 When was the last time you threw caution to the wind and said, "Why not?"?

2558 What was the last thing you were due to go to that had to be canceled or postponed?

2559 Should there be a Fortnite World Cup?

2560 What cheesy song makes you cry, even though it's lame?

2561 How would you tactfully tell a work colleague they had bad breath?

2562 What one thing should people stop accepting as normal?

2563 If the world wasn't a globe, what shape should it be?

2564 What everyday activity would you like to be able to fast-forward through?

2565 You're going backpacking. What one non-essential item would you carry in your backpack?

2566 What were you trying to do the last time you wished you had more than two hands?

2567 When you were a child, where did you think babies came from?

2568 What Ripley's *Believe It or Not* story do you find most difficult to believe?

2569 If you won a life-changing sum of money, what aspects of your life wouldn't change?

2570 What clubs or societies have you been a member of that you no longer attend?

2571 Have you ever been a sleepwalker? When was the last time?

2572 What hot food would be the most disgusting if eaten cold?

2573 "It's the End of the World as We Know It" is a song title. What event has made you think this way?

2574 Have you ever said yes when you should have said no?

2575 What will humans look like one million years from now?

2576 How far would you be prepared to travel to buy a hard-to-find item you need for a collection?

2577 What company or brand are you most loyal to? Why?

2578 If you could turn back time and purchase shares in one company, which one would it be? Why?

2579 Do you always brush your teeth in the same way?

2580 You have three wishes; what would the third one be?

2581 Do you believe life has been hard on you so far?

2582 What one thing should you never buy used?

2583 When was the last time you did the hokey pokey and where were you?

2584 If there could be only one pasta shape, what should it be?

2585 What type of cheese would you say is the best match for your style and personality?

2586 Humans share 99 percent of their DNA with chimpanzees. Judging by your habits, what might others think you share DNA with?

2587 Which TV game show would you most like to be a contestant on?

2588 Is there anything that can beat a cherry on top?

2589 What contraption from the Acme company in cartoons would be coolest to have in real life?

2590 Have you ever bought or read a self-help book? Which one?

2591 Which kids' TV show has messed up most young minds?

2592 If you were a bottle of wine, what three words would describe you on the label?

2593 What will the next wearable tech be?

2594 Could you stay off social media for a whole week?

2595 Who is the most inspirational person in your life?

2596 What conversation starter instantly lets you know someone isn't best buddy material?

2597 Have you ever lost all respect for someone? Who was it and why?

2598 What will you never, ever compromise on?

2599 When you were a child, what did you think you would never do as an adult that you now do?

2600 If we colonize the moon, what company will be the first to open for business up there?

2601 What's the weirdest diet you've ever gone on?

2602 How far would you be willing to commute for the job of your dreams?

2603 If you couldn't find a ruler, what would you use to draw a straight line with pen on paper?

2604 What household chores did you always do as a child? Did you get paid?

2605 You're going to do a daredevil leap across the Grand Canyon. What mode of transport will you use?

2606 What type of interior do you like a restaurant to have?

2607 How low can you go when you try to limbo?

2608 When was the last time you stormed out of a room, and why?

2609　What word do you always need to write down to check how to spell it?

2610　Do you believe in miracles? Why?

2611　If you couldn't use the word "awesome," what word would you use in its place?

2612　What type of person do you find most difficult to spend time with?

2613　If you're a brand, what's your tagline or mission statement?

2614　What everyday gadget would have been deemed witchcraft in medieval times?

2615　Have you ever lost your keys? Where did you find them?

2616　As a percentage, how happy are you with life right now?

2617　What are you determined to do, no matter what?

2618　When you were a baby, what was the best way to lull you to sleep?

2619　If you were a bus driver, at what point would you pull away if someone was running to get on?

2620　What one thing that is impossible today will become possible in the future?

2621　Have you ever lost your mojo? How did you get it back?

2622　What type of clouds are prettiest?

2623　If the story of your life was a book, what would its title be?

2624　What crime today will no longer be a crime in the future?

2625　Do you have a non-negotiable way of assembling a peanut butter and jelly sandwich?

2626　What road featured in a movie would you most like to take a trip down?

2627　If two items have the same specs and features, what makes you choose one brand over another?

2628　What everyday item keeps going missing in your home, but no one ever owns up to having taken it?

2629　Have you ever caught a snowflake on your tongue? When was the last time?

2630 What home workout equipment do you have? Do you ever use it?

2631 Should vaccinations be made mandatory? Why?

2632 What was the last thing you wished for when blowing out birthday candles?

2633 If you couldn't eat solid food for a week, what would you miss most?

2634 Which letter of the alphabet would you say is your favorite and why?

2635 When you think of home, what's the first thing that comes to mind?

2636 What world leader (past or present) would make the worst leader for your country, and why?

2637 Did you ever perform in a school play? What part did you play?

2638 What cool thing has become so popular that it's no longer cool?

2639 If the world was going to end tomorrow, would you want to know?

2640 What holiday tradition does your family maintain?

2641 Have you ever accidentally worn odd socks or shoes?

2642 What one thing that you forgot to do had the longest-lasting consequences?

2643 You're going to shave your head and rent your scalp out for advertising. What would you refuse to advertise?

2644 Do you know the actions that go with the "Baby Shark" song?

2645 When was the last time you exercised and what did you do?

2646 You have to choose one reality TV show to appear on. Which do you choose and why?

2647 What's your favorite song with a day of the week in the title or lyrics?

2648 Is there any type of cake that you couldn't manage to eat two generous slices of?

2649 Have you ever allowed someone else to take the blame for something you did? What was it?

2650 Have you had head lice? What's the weirdest head lice treatment you've heard of?

2651 What type of pizza crust is your first choice?

2652 If you were a butterfly, what colors would you be?

2653 What crazy cat video has made you laugh loudest?

2654 Can you say hello and goodbye in any other languages? Which ones?

2655 What's the weirdest example of taxidermy you've seen or heard of?

2656 If there could be only one color of pen, what should it be, and why?

2657 What daily task would be funniest if you had to do it at sloth speed?

2658 Have you ever lost your voice? How did you communicate?

2659 What type of scenery do you find most beautiful?

2660 Do you always stay within the lines when you're coloring in?

2661 When you meet someone new, what do you notice first?

2662 If you didn't want to be alone, who would you ask to come over?

2663 What was the last thing you wrote by hand?

2664 Have you ever buried anyone in sand at the beach?

2665 "Purple Rain" was a hit for Prince. What color rain would you like to see?

2666 What do you fear about getting older?

2667 Who is the most unlikely actor to play the next James Bond?

2668 If you're an anime fan, which one do (or did) you watch most?

2669 What's your favorite slang term for money?

2670 Have you ever said you liked something you'd never heard of just to impress someone? What was it?

2671 What creative thing could you make using empty egg cartons?

2672 Do you agree that seeing is believing?

2673 What hit song do you know all the dance moves for?

2674 Have you ever bounced on a Hoppity Hop (Space Hopper)? When was the last time?

2675 What daring thing would you do if you knew you wouldn't die doing it?

2676 When working out, do you prefer silence or sound (music, podcast, TV)? Why?

2677 Are you a perfectionist? If so, when does perfectionism strike most?

2678 What would be a creative name for mashed potatoes?

2679 Have you ever answered the phone and pretended to be someone else?

2680 What type of snake scares you most, and why?

2681 You're in a crowded place. How would you get the attention of a friend standing twenty feet away?

2682 Which three words would you use to describe your parents?

2683 How long was the longest wait you've ever had in a waiting room?

2684 What everyday thing that lots of people do have you never done?

2685 If there could only be one type of cake in the world, what should it be?

2686 What would be a deal breaker for you in a new job offer?

2687 When was the last time you stared longingly at an item in a shop window, and what was it?

2688 Do you always eat at the same times every day?

2689 What was in the coolest park you ever visited?

2690 If you were a cat, where would you sleep all day?

2691 What are you most afraid of?

2692 How high would you climb from the ground without wearing a safety harness?

2693 What would be a good name for baby octopuses?

2694 When was your last eureka or "aha!" moment?

2695 If you didn't have or couldn't get the job you wanted, what would be your second choice?

2696 What expression might replace "if pigs could fly" in a parallel universe?

2697 Have you ever broken someone's heart? Who and when?

2698 What design makes the best paper airplane?

2699 Can you imitate any animal noises? Which ones?

2700 What one thing will you never get used to?

2701 Have you ever bungee jumped? Where would you do it if given the chance?

2702 What was the last weird coincidence you experienced?

2703 How long was the longest game of Monopoly you ever played?

2704 Which member of the Beatles would you most like to have had lunch with?

2705 When was the last time you experienced pins and needles and where on your body?

2706 Is there an opportunity you feel you've missed and will never have again?

2707 What did the most ridiculous hat you've ever seen anyone wearing look like?

2708 If there had to be a sound attached to every step you took, what would you want it to be?

2709 What historical fashion (era or clothing) would you like to bring back?

2710 Should you always act your age, and what does that mean for you?

2711 What's your favorite shape and why?

2712 Do you have a party trick? What is it?

2713 What video game would make a great TV show?

2714 If you dinged someone's car in a parking lot, would you leave your contact details?

2715 What would be a good collective noun for a bunch of five-year-old kids?

2716 When was the last time you wrote a thank-you note, and who was it for?

2717 Have you ever met a celebrity and did they look different in real life?

2718 What was in the weirdest sandwich you ever made?

2719 You have to create a storefront window display for a department store. What theme will you use?

2720 Which TV commercial (good or bad) is the most memorable for you?

2721 If you fear the dark, what is it you think might be hiding in it?

2722 What herbal remedies do you swear by?

2723 Did you ever have a secret handshake or code that only you and your friends knew?

2724 What extra button would you like on your most-used remote control?

2725 If there is a parallel universe, what are you doing differently in it?

2726 What would be a good twenty-first-century update for the expression "strong as an ox"?

2727 When was the last time you spoke without thinking and what did you say?

2728 If there was such a thing as an inconvenience store, what would you be able to buy there?

2729 Have you ever met anyone from Australia named Bruce or Sheila?

2730 What date from history class sticks in your mind most?

2731 How long can you hold your breath for? How did you find out?

2732 What's the toughest interview question you've ever had to answer?

2733 If you found a bag of money on the street, what would you do?

2734 "Raindrops on roses and whiskers on kittens . . ." What are a few of your favorite things?

2735 What was on the best bumper sticker you've ever seen?

2736 Have you ever made a snow angel? When was the last time?

2737 What's your favorite rags to riches story?

2738 If you're bilingual, what language does the voice in your head speak?

2739 What would be a great alternative name for Frodo in *Lord of the Rings?*

2740 When was the last time you wore galoshes (rubber boots)?

2741 You're invited to a teddy bears' picnic. What teddy will you take?

2742 What expressions used by teenagers today are most confusing for the older generation?

2743 Do you always stick by the ten-second rule if you drop food on the floor?

2744 What road sign that doesn't exist do you think should exist?

2745 If you found a fly in your soup in a restaurant, would you stay for the next course?

2746 Who is the noisiest person you know?

2747 What would be a great noise for a toaster to make to let you know your toast is ready?

2748 Have you ever said, "There must be more to life than this," and what were you doing at the time?

2749 If you were a caped crusader, what color would your cape be?

2750 What was the last word you looked up in a dictionary?

2751 At what age did you leave your parents' home, or at what age should you leave home?

2752 What devices have you fixed recently by switching them off and switching them on again?

2753 Have you ever organized a surprise party for anyone?

2754 What one thing will you never give up on?

2755 You're in the shower, the door is locked, and you see a snake slither out of the toilet. What would you do?

2756 What would be a more creative name for peanut butter?

2757 If you were a celebrity chef, what would your signature dish be?

2758 What extinct animal would you most like to bring back?

2759 How long was the longest flight you've been on and where were you going?

2760 What was the big playground craze when you were a kid? Were you into it?

2761 If you found a secret passage in your home, where would you like it to lead?

2762 Do you always choose the easy option?

2763 What healthy version of a food tastes better than the unhealthy version of the food?

2764 Wardrobe malfunction! You've popped a button on your pants. What do you use to hold them up?

2765 When was the last time you woke up with a start in the night? Why?

2766 If *Thomas the Tank Engine* was given a twenty-first century revamp, what modern names might the engines be given?

2767 What was the first card trick you learned how to do?

2768 How long do you wait for a web page to download before you give up and move on?

2769 What are you most likely to choose to eat from an Indian restaurant menu?

2770 If you found a wedding ring on a sidewalk, what would you do?

2771 What's your favorite pickled food?

2772 Have you ever been a pet sitter for a friend? What animal did you look after?

2773 What would be a creative name for the pit in the crook of your elbow?

2774 When was the last time you fell flat on your face?

2775 What famous mystery would you most like to be able to solve?

2776 If you're having trouble getting to sleep, what fun thing might you count instead of sheep?

2777 You need a shock-and-awe outfit to wear at a red-carpet event. What is it?

2778 What was on the last list you made?

2779 If you found buried treasure at the bottom of your garden, what would you want it to be?

2780 Why doesn't glue stick to the inside of the tube?

2781 Are you ambidextrous? When do you, or would you, find it most useful?

2782 Which member of the British royal family would you most like to meet?

2783 If you had a bucket list of things NOT to do in life, what would you put on there?

2784 What would be an appropriate made up collective noun for a group of teenagers?

2785 Have you ever bought two identical items of clothing and only worn one? What was it?

2786 What did you buy with your first paycheck or money you earned doing a job?

2787 If there's life on another planet, what does it look like?

2788 What's your favorite pick at a Pizza Hut salad bar?

2789 Do you have a pen that's also a flashlight? What other gizmo combos do you have?

2790 What was the most awesome graffiti you've ever seen?

2791 Have you ever been able to do any yo-yo tricks? Which ones?

2792 What have you tried to do that you discovered you were terrible at doing?

2793 Do you strike a pose when someone takes a picture of you? What's that pose?

2794 What was the first alcoholic drink you tried, and how old were you?

2795 You have to provide a spontaneous fun fact about anything. What is it?

2796 What did you do as a child that you absolutely would not do now?

2797 If you were a champion snowboarder, what would your signature trick be?

2798 When was the last time you saw sunrise, and where were you?

2799 What rock song would sound most awesome sung by a barbershop quartet?

2800 Have you ever saved coins in a piggy bank? How much did you save?

2801 What's the weirdest contest you've ever heard of?

2802 Should you fake it until you make it? Have you done that?

2803 What did you last daydream about?

2804 Can you do an underwater handstand? When was the last time?

2805 What would be the best thing about being a monkey for the day?

2806 When was the last time you were in trouble, and why?

2807 Have you ever owned a Tamagotchi?

2808 What was the first curse word you dared to use in front of your parents?

2809 If you're the hero in your life story, who is the main villain?

2810 Do you always follow the same morning routine? What happens if it's interrupted?

2811 What one thing would you miss most about the area you live in if you had to move far away?

2812 "Taco cat" is a palindrome (spelled the same backward as forward). What other palindromes do you know?

2813 War: what is it good for?

2814 What would be the most awesome and ridiculous thing to row across the Atlantic In?

2815 If you had a CB radio, what would your handle be (good buddy)?

2816 Which three websites do you visit most often?

2817 Do you always guess who did it in a whodunnit story?

2818 What have you seen or heard recently to restore your faith in humanity?

2819 If there was a fifth Ninja Turtle, what would their name be?

2820 What was the first horror movie you saw?

2821 If there were no cats on Earth, what would replace cat videos on the internet?

2822 What would be the downside of being immortal?

2823 Were your schooldays the happiest days of your life? Why?

2824 Is there an item of clothing in your closet that you haven't worn in the last year?

2825 What would be the most boring pet to have?

2826 Who is the oldest person you know?

2827 What fashion or trend will never become outdated?

2828 Have you ever said, "It's not you, it's me" to anyone, and how did they take it?

2829 When was the last time you watched a DVD? What was it?

2830 What would be the most difficult part of your day if you couldn't bend your knees?

2831 If you had a fairy godmother, what one magic spell would you like her to do for you?

2832 What did you do when you realized "the cavalry ain't coming" to help you?

2833 How hot is too hot?

2834 What did you spend most of your allowance on as a child?

2835 Do you always make your bed in the morning? If not, what's the longest it has gone unmade?

2836 What would be the most ridiculous car for the Incredible Hulk to drive?

2837 If toothpaste wasn't minty, what flavor should it be?

2838 When was the last time you felt alone in a crowd?

2839 What was the first movie you ever saw in a movie theater?

2840 Have you ever been camping, and where did you go?

2841 What would be the worst choice of song for a first dance at a wedding?

2842 If you had a hot air balloon, what design or message would you print on it?

2843 What's your favorite orange-flavored thing?

2844 Could you perform CPR (cardiopulmonary resuscitation) in an emergency? Have you ever needed to?

2845 What have you most recently experienced for the first time?

2846 How long (time or miles) was the longest walk you've been on?

2847 What was the most boring event you've ever had to attend?

2848 If you had a personal assistant for a day, what would you have them do?

2849 What would be the worst non-monetary prize you personally could win on a game show?

2850 Have you ever made a big mistake that no one ever found out about—until now?

2851 What would be the worst smell for a scratch-n-sniff product?

2852 If you're told not to think of pink elephants, what do you think about?

2853 What are you most looking forward to tomorrow?

2854 Is there an emoji you'll never use?

2855 Do you believe in reincarnation? What would you like to return as?

2856 Which member of your family do you talk with the most?

2857   If you had a personal chef to cook your next meal, what would you order?

2858   Which three qualities make someone a good boss?

2859   Have you ever made the same mistake twice? What was it?

2860   What did you spend on the most expensive pair of sneakers you ever bought?

2861   At a guess, how many Pringles could you fit in your mouth at once?

2862   What role would Keanu Reeves play in the movie of your life?

2863   Have you ever boycotted a product because the TV commercial annoyed you?

2864   What fate would you not wish on your worst enemy?

2865   If you had a secret bunker, what would be in it?

2866   When was the last time you walked into a room and forgot why you went in there?

2867   What would be the worst type of food to store in your pocket for later?

2868   Do you have a possession that you wouldn't let someone borrow? What is it?

2869   What discovery would you like to be famous for making?

2870   You must choose between your two absolute favorite desserts. How do you choose?

2871   Where would you absolutely not move to, even if you were offered the job of your dreams there?

2872   What have you learned today?

2873   If you had all the time and Lego bricks in the world, what would you build?

2874   What was the first joke you ever learned?

2875   Have you ever met a "Karen" who was actually called Karen?

2876   What's your favorite music platform?

2877   If you had an accident and had to go to the hospital, who would you want to go with you?

2878 What one word best describes your childhood bedroom?

2879 Did you ever keep tadpoles in a jar as a kid?

2880 What's the weirdest combination of items you've ever put through a grocery store checkout?

2881 If there's one thing you're a sucker for, what is it?

2882 What was the naughtiest thing you did as a kid?

2883 How long does a perfect boiled egg need to boil for?

2884 What DIY skill would you most like to have?

2885 Someone at your workplace or school is not who they say they are. Who do you suspect?

2886 What fashionable thing of today will become old-fashioned first?

2887 Have you ever been caught in the rain and completely drenched?

2888 Which three letters on a keyboard do you use most?

2889 Is there an actor that appears in every movie you haven't liked? Who?

2890 What was the first thing you thought about when you woke up this morning?

2891 If you could trade places with a family member or friend for a day, who would you pick and what would you do?

2892 What would be your perfect personal hangout spot, and where would it be?

2893 If you were a daredevil juggler, what three or more items would you juggle with in your act?

2894 When was the last time you saw a lightning storm?

2895 What would be your weapon of choice in a zombie apocalypse?

2896 If you're to be known by just one of your character traits, which one would you like it to be?

2897 Could dinosaurs and humans have coexisted on Earth?

2898   What's your favorite topic on YouTube to watch?

2899   Have you ever owned a Sony cassette-based Walkman?

2900   What have you heard recently that shocked you?

2901   If you had cat-like agility, what would you do with it?

2902   What did your parents think was just a phase you were going through, but you're still into it now?

2903   Does the idea of public speaking scare you? Have you done it?

2904   What rooftop would you most like to sit on to watch the world go by?

2905   When was the last time you vomited?

2906   What would it take for you to have a perfect day?

2907   ABBA is an acronym of the band members' first names. What three friends could you make a band name with?

2908   What's your favorite Mexican food?

2909   If your body was made of Play-Doh, would you reshape it?

2910   Who is the rudest person you've ever met? How were they rude?

2911   What was the first video game you played?

2912   If you had hair like Rapunzel, how would you style it?

2913   What would make the funniest replacements for an egg and spoon in a race?

2914   Have you ever shrunk anything in the wash? What was it?

2915   When was the last time you felt cheated?

2916   If there were only two kittens left in the litter, would you still take just one?

2917   What's the weirdest coincidence you've read or heard about?

2918   Do you always read the small print and terms and conditions before clicking "accept"?

2919 What would make a good alternative saying for "the black sheep of the family"?

2920 Have you ever been caught picking your nose?

2921 What faux animal pelt would make the most ridiculous rug?

2922 Can you talk in rhyme? At what point does it stop being funny?

2923 What would the blurb on the back cover of your memoirs say?

2924 If there were six Spice Girls, what spice name would you give the sixth one?

2925 What's your favorite meat-free meal?

2926 Have you ever parked in a disabled parking space without a permit?

2927 What disease would you least like to be told you had?

2928 If you had identical twins, would you dress them in identical outfits?

2929 What would you add to existing roller coasters to make the best ever roller coaster?

2930 Steak in a toaster? Who is the laziest cook you know?

2931 When was the last time you used the stairs instead of the elevator?

2932 Do you always say what you mean and mean what you say?

2933 What was the last random thought you had in the shower?

2934 If you were a circus performer, what would your act be?

2935 Which member of your family is the most clueless about technology?

2936 Have you ever broken a safety rule? What was it?

2937 What would you advise everyone never to wipe their butt with?

2938 Can you imagine a situation in which you might consider cannibalism to stay alive? What would it be?

2939 What are you not afraid of now that you were afraid of when you were younger?

2940 Have you ever played a non-lethal version of Russian roulette? What was it?

2941 What do people get overly upset about that they really shouldn't?

2942 If you were a dish on an expensive restaurant menu, how would you describe yourself?

2943 What's the worst thing you've had stuck on the sole of your shoe?

2944 When was the last time you said "What was I thinking?" and why?

2945 What would you carry if it all had to be carried in a red-and-white spotted hanky tied onto a stick?

2946 Do you have a routine way to wash yourself in the shower or bath?

2947 What was the subject of the most impressive ice sculpture you've ever seen?

2948 Is there a word you sometimes have difficulty saying? What is it?

2949 What was the last big decision you had to make?

2950 How long does it take you to get ready for work (school) each morning?

2951 Which three foods would you always peel before eating?

2952 What would you do if you found $500 in an envelope left behind on a bus?

2953 Have you ever seen a fake so good you were convinced it was real?

2954 What have you had to wait a long time for but was totally worth it?

2955 You lose your bathing suit while swimming in the sea. What do you do?

2956 What was the last book you read and how would you score it out of ten?

2957 Did you ever have your face painted as a child? What was your favorite face?

2958 What have you felt guilty about recently?

2959 How long have you had the oldest item of clothing you still wear?

2960 What's your favorite long-lost pet reunion story?

2961 If you had no cups or mugs in the house, what would you use for hot drinks?

2962 What was the last straw for you?

2963 Have you ever seen a solar eclipse?

2964 What would you do if you found a raccoon in your kitchen?

2965 When was the last time you used a sweeping broom, and what were you sweeping?

2966 What one word could you use to describe your mom?

2967 Do you still use the same social media platforms today that you used a year ago?

2968 What routine habit or practice in your home might visitors find a little odd?

2969 Have you ever sent a text message to the wrong person? What happened?

2970 What fictional family would be the worst to have as your real family?

2971 At what point in your life did you feel the greatest peer pressure?

2972 What would you do if you heard a tornado warning?

2973 When was the last time you traveled by train and where were you going?

2974 Starsky and Hutch? Cagney and Lacey? What names would make a cool-sounding cop duo?

2975 What plants or flowers would you grow in your ideal garden?

2976 How long should the tea bag stay in water to make the perfect cup of tea?

2977 What would you like to see commemorated on a coin?

2978 Do you always sleep in the same position? If so, what is it?

2979 What's the weirdest app you've heard of?

2980 When was the last time you felt envious of someone?

2981 What would you most like to win a lifetime supply of?

2982 If you had one extra hour every day, what would you do with it?

2983 What do bears eat at a teddy-bear's picnic?

2984 Have you ever broken anything in a shop and had to pay for it?

2985 What do you worry about that other people tell you not to worry about?

2986 If you were a dog, would you hold the record for holding the most tennis balls in your mouth?

2987 What was the subject of the most interesting conversation you've had this week?

2988 Which movie title becomes the most ridiculous if you tag "versus zombies" onto the end of it?

2989 Can you solve a Rubik's Cube, and if so, how fast and in how many moves?

2990 What was the last thing someone had to forgive you for?

2991 If you had quadruplets, what would you name them?

2992 What would you say is a stereotypical American food?

2993 Who is the weirdest person that ever sat next to you on a bus, train, or plane?

2994 What do people quarrel about the most?

2995 Is there a word you always have difficulty spelling correctly? What is it?

2996 What would make the most romantic marriage proposal ever?

2997 Which three famous people (past or present) would you most like to play a game of Twister with?

2998 What have you grown out of that you thought you never would?

2999 Do you have a sixth sense, and how would you explain it to others?

3000 What was the last thing someone said or did that you were offended by?

About Us

We're an odd bunch of fun, quirky, and creative authors who love writing thought-provoking questions on a mission to spark engaging discussions.

We've all experienced awkward silence situations and resorted to superficial chitchat and small talk to pass time.

The authors here at Questions About Me are on a mission to end dull conversations. We created the Unique Questions About Me series to invigorate conversations and help you get to know people better ...even yourself.

Put down your phone, switch off the TV, and use our Questions About Me series of books as prompts to unlock endless conversational possibilities, create an abundance of fun memories, and develop deeper relationships.

www.questionsaboutme.com

Before You Go

Thank you for purchasing our Questions About Me book series.

We'd really love to hear your thoughts on our books. Your comments really help us, the Questions About Me authors and also, other readers what you think of our books.

It's really easy to submit your feedback, simply visit the link below.
Click on the image of the book and then click on the stars.

You can also share your thoughts about the book, even if it's just a sentence or two.

www.amazon.com/ryp

Printed in Great Britain
by Amazon

35550011R00088